BOOKS BY *Kay Boyle*

THE Smoking
MOUNTAIN

THE Smoking MOUNTAIN

Stories of
Germany during the Occupation

BY

KAY BOYLE

With a Foreword by WILLIAM L. SHIRER

New York : Alfred·A·Knopf

1 9 6 8

GRATEFUL ACKNOWLEDGMENT is made to *The New Yorker* for permission to reprint the "Introduction," originally published in somewhat different form as "The People with Names," "Begin Again," "Fife's House," "Summer Evening," "The Criminal," and "Adam's Death"; and to the following magazines in which the other stories first appeared: *Harper's Magazine* for "Home" and "Aufwiedersehen Abend," *The Nation* for "Frankfurt in Our Blood" and "The Lovers of Gain," and *Tomorrow* for "Cabaret" and "The Lost."

L. C. catalog card number: 63–9120

THIS IS A BORZOI BOOK
PUBLISHED BY ALFRED A. KNOPF, INC.

This collection of stories was first published by McGraw-Hill Book Company, Inc., in 1951.

BORZOI EDITION PUBLISHED MARCH 18, 1963
SECOND PRINTING, JULY 1968

"Wretched German people, you built cities, built cathe-drals, placed free tillers on a free soil, reached lofty heights in art, in science, in law, in languages. You evolved the Hansa, evolved guilds, evolved free crafts, found manifold modes of expression for your nature. Your military organization can only be considered as one aspect of your complex social constitution. That de-partment expanded, grew all-powerful, swallowed up everything else. It broke down all dikes and flooded over the boundaries of other countries, and the tiller had to leave his soil, the workman his work, the priest his parish, the teacher his pupils, the youth his companions, the hus-band his wife; the people ceased to exist as a people and became nothing but fuel for the monstrous, smoking mountain, the individual became nothing but wood, peat, fuel oil, and finally a black flake spewed up out of the flames."

THEODOR PLIEVIER

Foreword

BY

WILLIAM L. SHIRER

An English historian recently remarked that if a German really looks at recent German history he is almost bound to cut his throat.

That is a very English—and American—point of view. But it is not a typical German one. There has been no slashing of throats in Germany over this concern. Most Germans in the Nineteen Sixties do not give much thought to their recent history, and they deeply—and sometimes, hysterically—resent foreign writers who in the interest of history try to recall it as it was.

We must try to understand the reason for this. The Nazi past does not loom in German minds and hearts as nearly so evil and barbarous as non-Germans have felt it to be. In fact, the vast majority of Germans—so far as I could see on the spot at the time—found life in the Third Reich quite to their liking. The men at the top of the old German institutions and professions, with very few exceptions, not only went along with Adolf Hitler and his brown-shirted thugs: they abetted them, helping them in many instances to grab power in Germany and then, with scarcely a twinge, to destroy civilization first in the Reich and then over most of Nazi-occupied Europe.

The German masses went along too, often with roars of enthusiasm which still din in my ears nearly three decades later. Why not? Hitler was giving the German people what they wanted: work, prosperity, profits, conquest. He was wiping out the shame of defeat in World War I by freeing the nation from the "shackles" of the Versailles peace *Diktat*. He was making Germany militarily mighty again. The Germans did not seem to me to mind very much that the dictator was at the same time robbing them of their freedoms.

It should therefore not have caused the surprise it did in the Western Democracies that even after the war, when Nazi rule had brought the Fatherland to utter ruin, the majority of the German people could look back across the wasteland of rubble and of the millions of dead and maimed and affirm—as it did in the public-opinion polls month after month, year after year—that on the whole Nazism had been a good thing.

Is it any wonder then that so many Germans resented the denazification proceedings introduced by the victorious Allies after the war? Miss Boyle, in one of the short stories in this memorable book, describes the high feeling of the townspeople against a denazification trial of a former Nazi newspaper editor. The story, like the others in this volume, is based on what the author actually saw in Germany toward the close of the Nineteen Forties, and in a factual note in the Introduction she tells us, without raising her voice in surprise, that the real-life Nazi editor soon founded a new newspaper of his own, circumventing Occupation regulations by publishing it in his son's name. No use raising an eyebrow. Such things happened all over post-Nazi Germany in the denazification time.

Indeed the great bestseller in democratic West Germany at this time was the book *Der Fragebogen,* which heaped scorn and ridicule on the whole denazification business. The author, Ernst von Salomon, was a right-wing German extremist who had served a prison sentence for complicity in the murder of Walther Rathenau during the early days of the ill-fated Weimar Republic.

The good people of West Germany snatched up the book as fast as copies came off the printing presses. They seemed to find in the author's defiance, in his thumbing the nose at the occupiers, an expression of their own deep pent-up feelings, though it was in truth—or so it seemed to me—a rather silly book by a mediocre writer whose credentials at this stage in German history seemed to an outsider, at least, somewhat questionable.

Most of Kay Boyle's novels and short stories were written in France, where she lived for some twenty years. France, I imagine, was her second love, as it was for so many of us back in the wild and golden Twenties when the American writers flocked to Paris and when almost any evening on the terrace of a Montparnasse café or at Lipp's at St. Germain-des-Prés you could run into such persons as Hemingway, Dos Passos, MacLeish, Fitzgerald, Hart Crane, Sinclair Lewis, Glenway Wes-

cott, Harry Crosby, Eugene Jolas, Harold Stearns, Louis Brom-
field, Kay Boyle, Matthew Josephson, E. E. Cummings, Ezra
Pound, and many others, including Malcolm Cowley, who later
would chronicle their doings on the left bank of the Seine.
Like as not, some of the above mentioned, before coming to
the café, had just come from a session with Gertrude Stein
around the corner at her home near the Luxembourg gardens.

Most of these writers are now dead, having made a greater
or a lesser contribution to the most creative era in American
writing. Kay Boyle, one of the very few women in the group,
continues uninterruptedly to write, and the body of her work,
written with a delicacy of style and mood that has the stamp
of genius, has grown into a substantial and lasting achievement.

Back in the somewhat zany Twenties, Miss Boyle, it is true,
joined a number of other writers in signing the famous "Procla-
mation" that launched Jolas's left-bank *transition* and in which
was proclaimed not only the "revolution" of the word but the
"hallucination" of the word (whatever that means) and in
which the twelfth and last "proposition" stated: "The plain
reader be damned!" Actually I can remember nothing in Miss
Boyle's novels and short stories—nor is there anything in this
volume—that damned the "plain reader," if such there be.

Unlike so many of her former left-bank fellow-writers, she
has taken an active interest not only in literature but in the
political and social events and issues of our time, generating in
her attempt to understand them the same passion she has had
for fiction. Some writers are proud to eschew politics and to
remain uninvolved and uncommitted in the sad state of affairs
in this world. But since Hitler—or since Lenin, Stalin, and
Khrushchev—how could one, even if he were a creative writer?
In a world tottering on the edge of nuclear extinction, has a

writer more right than others to poke his head in the sand?
Not in the opinion of Kay Boyle. I think she would agree that
a writer has less right than many others.

It is important for the readers of this volume to understand the
state of mind of the author when, after two decades of living
and working in France, she moved in the spring of 1948 to
Germany, where her Austrian-born husband had a post in the
American Occupational government as an official of the United
States War Department. Though she had often visited Germany, beginning as a child and continuing up through the Nazi
time, she tells us that the Germans she knew best were exiles.
They had fled, as she says, not from an invader but from their
own people.

No writer going to live and work among the Germans for
the first time has been more frank and honest about her feelings. She had committed herself, she states, to a "painstaking
and almost completely loveless search for another face of Germany"—the face, that is, which perhaps had been hidden by
the howling of the Nazis. I say "perhaps" because Miss Boyle
really didn't know whether there was another face. She was
skeptical. She did not feel herself, as she so strikingly puts it,
"authorized for a single, hesitant instant" to forget the ignoble
immediate past of Germany. This was really the only way to
begin.

For until she and we and, most of all, the Germans understood how it happened that an ancient, apparently civilized,
cultured, Christian nation in the twentieth century organized
and carried out the senseless cold-blooded massacre of five million Jews and of millions more of non-Jews, mostly Slavs, there

can be little comprehension of this people, either past or present, by themselves or by the rest of us.

The answer to the question of how it could happen, and did happen, is admittedly difficult to come by. And the searcher for truth, as Miss Boyle is in this book, is not helped very much by the glib answers of most Germans today—from Chancellor Adenauer on down—who try to perpetrate the myth that only a few bad Germans had anything to do with Hitler's evil regime and even fewer with his evil acts.

I suspect that non-German historians such as Hugh Trevor-Roper and Raul Hilberg are getting nearer to the truth. Pondering as he has for years the problem of responsibility for the Nazi genocide, Trevor-Roper recently (in 1962) concluded that "this unique, purposeless, but systematic crime was not the work of a party. It was a national act. Disguise it as they may the Germans were involved in it as a nation." Hilberg, in his massive, documented study, *The Destruction of the European Jews*, agrees. "However one may wish to draw the line of active participation," he concludes, "the machinery of destruction was a remarkable cross-section of the German population."

No wonder Miss Boyle did not feel herself "authorized for a single, hesitant instant" to forget it as she began to mingle with the Germans a bare four years after the furnaces of Auschwitz had finally run out of fuel and cooled.

Also, she had read German history, philosophy, novels, and poetry. She had read Goethe, Nietzsche, Heine, and Thomas Mann. And she had been struck, as they had been, great Germans all, by the duality of German identity.

Goethe had stated it in the now famous words: "I have often felt a bitter sorrow at the thought of the German people, which is so estimable in the individual and so wretched in the generality." Nietzsche and Heine, whose opinion of their fellow Germans was not very high, were prime examples of the duality of the German mind and soul. Miss Boyle ponders them and their writings as she enters Germany.

This is the Germany of 1948 and it is not a pretty place for human beings, either the conquered or the conquerors. The cities are largely a mass of ruins, the rubble piled high wherever you look. The Germans, who have lost another great war they expected to win, are understandably still in a daze. They tend to bow and scrape to their not always well-mannered American conquerors, for whom they find it difficult not to feel deep down a certain contempt as well as envy.

It is a time when American cigarettes are still the best of currencies, especially between G.I.'s and German girls, when most Germans are hungry, ill-clothed, cold, and full of self-pity, when most Americans—in the army or in the government of Occupation—are sated with food and drink and are living comfortably (better than many did at home) amid the ruins in splendid isolation from the Germans, whose language they do not know and cannot or will not learn and whose past and even present they little understand. In this book Miss Boyle writes not only about Germans but about Americans in Germany, not sparing the truth about either.

It is a Germany which no longer exists. The rubble has long since been cleared, the cities and factories rebuilt, the Germans become prosperous and independent and confident, their former American conquerors now their allies, their well-wishers, indeed their champions in the affairs of Europe.

One value of Miss Boyle's book is that it paints an unforgettable picture of the Germans in that bitter time of adversity. They live a better life now. The question is have they them-

selves changed? Obviously they have changed since the first
grim postwar years when merely to keep alive absorbed most
of their energies. They are once again proud citizens of a
booming, strong, sovereign Germany. But are they different
from what they were in the Nazi time when for sufficient reasons they made Germany the most hated country in Europe?

Miss Boyle's book was published in 1951 and it appears here
as it was written then. But the questions she raised at the beginning of the Nineteen Fifties still persist in the Nineteen
Sixties. They are questions she has explored as well in *Generation Without Farewell*, a novel set in occupied Germany and
published in 1960. Some of these questions she puts herself;
others she gets from Germans.

They pop up in the long Introduction, which consists mostly
of her brilliant coverage for *The New Yorker* of the trial in
the Spring of 1950 at Frankfurt of a small-time Eichmann
named Heinrich Baab. This S.S. Gestapo officer had been indicted on a charge of participating in fifty-six cases of murder
in Frankfurt in the Nazi time. As with Eichmann, he was not
charged with the actual murder of Jews but with aiding and
abetting and participating in murder. His defense was the same
as Eichmann's. "I am not guilty of the death of these people,"
he told the court. "My actions were all within legal bounds,
and were performed on the orders of my superiors."

It is an old and by now familiar song. But this trial was different from the later one in Jerusalem in that it was an all-
German affair, prepared and conducted by Germans. "It was,"
Miss Boyle tells us, "as if the will of the German people was
putting on trial in a German courtroom, before German judges
and a German jury, the actual substance of Germany's other
reality."

As she sits in the courtroom day after day that spring, the author is beset by questions rising in her mind. Of what, and of how many, she asks, was this man Baab a representative? For how many had he acted? She put the questions to "gently bred Germans," who assured her that this Gestapo killer was no more representative of Germany than Al Capone was of America. And yet?

> But there is one factor which must set them apart forever, and that is that Baab functioned as an official, with official sanction.

That is getting at the heart of the answer we seek and which non-German writers like Trevor-Roper and Hilberg have emphasized. Those who carried out the Nazi massacres were not just gangsters acting on a sadistic impulse to kill the helpless when not killing for gain. They were German officials carrying out the orders of the government of a great nation, a government which had unified the German people for the first time in their history, and which had the support of most citizens. The support not for these outrageous crimes of mass slaughter of human beings, to be sure. But a support that was general and so strong that when the crimes occurred the protest of the good Germans, as Miss Boyle observes, was never audible.

When a protest is so feeble that it cannot even be heard, of what worth is it?

Many Germans argue that the people didn't know what was really going on and that this fact accounts for the lack of strong protest. No doubt millions didn't know exactly, though they were aware of the concentration camps and the deportation of the Jews, and this knowledge might have given them pause for thought.

But a lot of Germans did know. The officers and soldiers of the army knew. They saw the S.S. Einsatzgruppen in action in Russia, mowing down their victims with machine guns by the side of previously dug burial pits. Indeed Himmler and Heydrich and Kaltenbrunner, the chiefs of the S.S. Gestapo, made a point of keeping the Army High Command fairly up to date on their doings.

The German bureaucracy knew. Thousands of its officials were busy organizing the slaughter. It was, after all, a big project. Complex. A hundred and one details. Just to transport millions of persons from all over Europe to the death camps was quite an undertaking. Think of all the trains with how many thousands of boxcars and hundreds of locomotives and train crews!

Many businessmen knew. Some of them were bidding spiritedly for contracts to supply the gas chambers, the gas, and the ovens. Krupp and I. G. Farben, two of Germany's greatest business concerns, whose directors had long been among the pillars of German society—and who still are—set up factories at Auschwitz, where Jewish slave labor was employed until it was worked out and became eligible for the gas chambers nearby.

These Germans knew—in the army, in the bureaucracy, in business. Unlike their counterparts in Fascist Italy, they went along with the grizzly business. Some made profits from it. Some of these are back in business today, not in a grizzly business, just in business. Krupp and I. G. Farben no longer operate factories manned by expendable Jewish or other slave labor. But they are prospering and their association with the Federal government in Bonn is close and amicable.

And the few surviving Jews of Germany? Are they spared

at last of the anti-Semitism which sent most of their relatives to death in the gas chambers? In a novelist's way, Miss Boyle raises the question in one of her short stories here—and partly answers it.

A Mrs. Furley reaches the meat counter at the American Commissary and chats with the German working behind it. In better times he had been a theatre producer and once, he tells her, he had worked with an American director, "a Jew from New York but a nice Jew."

"Why do you say 'a nice Jew'?" asked Mrs. Furley.

The narrator steps in to reply.

But the answer had already been given in the history of the country, and nothing that had been said since had been said with power or passion enough to take that answer away.

Though Kay Boyle has made her reputation largely from her novels and short stories, you will also find a superb reporter here—both in the factual account of the Baab trial and in the short stories that follow. Her powers of description are the envy of an old reporter. Her first sight of the prisoner Baab in the dock moves her to write an indelible portrait of the wretched man that lingers in the mind long after the book has been finished.

No short story that I can remember opens with such an impact as the first paragraphs of "The Lovers of Gain." It fixes for all time the feeling of defeated Germany in those rubble-strewn first postwar years.

The days in Germany were like the days in no other country, there to be breathed into being as one might breathe into the lips and nostrils of the dead. The hours of them seemed suspended, perhaps brought to a halt by the monumental rubble, but halted so long ago that it could no longer be recalled in what month, or year, or even in what lifetime, their sequence had reached this pause. Perhaps the bleak Teutonic twilight had set in as the reverberations of the final bomb faded to silence in the ruins . . . Perhaps the meaning of night and day, of summer and winter, of peace and war, had been lost to this country in the instant when the last hope of German victory had died.

This book captures those days in Germany which were unlike the days in any other country. They are gone, a passing moment of German history. But Miss Boyle implants them in our memory, there to be stored for as long as we shall live.

Contents

T H E Smoking
MOUNTAIN

Introduction

Iɴ ᴛʜᴇ sᴘʀɪɴɢ of 1948, I left France—a country I had made my home in for nearly twenty years—and I came to live, and write, in Germany. I came without eagerness, abhorring this country's immediate past, knowing that those Germans who had been free and fearless men had, in our time, been exterminated by their countrymen, or else that one had known them as refugees on foreign soil. I had visited Germany during several summers as a child; and I had come briefly to Germany in 1935, and 1936, and again in 1938, after the Anschluss with Austria had taken place. The Germans I knew were those who had fled, and fled not from an invader but from their own people, and who still preferred to remain in exile after the war was through. In early 1947, I returned to visit Displaced Persons' camps in the American Zone, and in that year I talked with many Germans, from street cleaners to university professors, the residue of a police state; and, as I listened to their stories of individual, if unwilling, acceptance of that state, I remembered the quality of French and Spanish acceptance of the individual obligations to liberty. And then, in 1948, I came to live here, and, by so doing, committed myself to a painstaking and almost completely loveless search for another face of Germany.

The mere act of entering this occupied country imposes inexorable demands upon the heart and reason. If one is, both as human being and recorder, to clear a way through the complex and ignoble history of what took place, one is not authorized for a single, hesitant instant to forget the meaning of those issues which were so truly comprehended during and after Germany's military defeat. Time or emotion may not be permitted to deform by their insidious power the perspective in which these issues were first seen. If it be asked what force withholds this authorization, the answer is one's belief that man is given a choice, and that the choice is not to be evaded, but made. Yet, faced with the colossal ruins of cities which have been seventy, or eighty, or ninety, or ninety-five, per cent destroyed, the mind no longer recognizes cause and effect, and the explanation of why this had to take place is reduced to a monstrous absurdity. Thus, it is one's own reason which must set the limits as to what time and emotion may be permitted to accomplish, so that pity may be allowed its full measure of human tenderness, but nothing more. I believe there is an impulse far more compassionate than the act of experiencing compassion. After the first shock and sense of outrage at the sight of this monumental destruction, it is essential that the true computation be fervently made. For one comes to know, without pity, that the ruthless cause which produced these effects is still intact if only these walls, whose substance the hands can touch, have been destroyed.

As I attempt to set down my own evaluation of what I have found in my brief two years here, I am aware that all the analyses of this country, and the proclivities of its people, have been made. For decades, German philosophers and German poets and men of letters have wrung their disavowal of the German people from the depths of their commitment to that people. Among these were Goethe, Heine, Nietzsche, Mann, Plievier; and in their denunciation of, as in their dedication to, the German people they came by separate, even by antithetical, ways to the recognition of a single, fatal thing. Each came to his own separate vision of the duality of German identity, and, baffled, each sought to probe within that vision. "The Germans are more intangible, more ample, more contradictory, more unknown, more incalculable, more surprising, and even more terrifying than other people are to themselves. . . ." Nietzsche wrote nearly a century ago—Nietzsche who, in himself, has given us the perfect symbol of German man, of man divided within himself, unable to comprehend and judge himself because unable to see himself in his entirety. "German and Jew, patriot and Francophile," David Daiches has written of Heinrich Heine, "sentimentalist and ironist, radical and hater of the organized left, Christian convert and passionate defender of Israel, charlatan and martyr, lyrical poet and journalist, lover of life and perpetual self-torturer— his haunting figure looms out of the mists of social and ideological conflict in early nineteenth century Europe to appear as the epitome of all the problems that face sensitive man today." Was Germany then, one comes to ask oneself as one lives here in its ruins, offered as warning, and the people of Germany, Jews and Christians alike, sacrificed so that their drama might serve as admonition to the modern world? Are the dual propensities of the German identity to be taken, then, as symbols for the choice each man is offered, and how much—or how tragically little—of the drama have we officially understood?

I have heard Americans in official positions here say that in the beginning of the Nazi regime, before the brutalities became widespread, there was about as much difference between the Nazis and the non-Nazis as between Republicans and Democrats at home. It might be possible to find something humorous in this definition did it not express the essence of our failure in comprehension here. We have never wished to believe that the choice was not a political, but a moral one, a choice between good and evil in the profoundest sense, but there is ample evidence that the Germans themselves know this was true. A spokesman for a nationalistic party stated recently that "had Hitler adhered to the traditional ideas of the *Rechtsstaat*, we would have had no war and would be quite satisfied, except for the solution of the racial question." Even more recently, the West German Chancellor, Dr. Konrad Adenauer, publicly declared that the time had come "for Germans to end the division of the people into sinners and innocents"; for *Germans*, he specified, knowing more bitterly and more certainly than any foreigner can know it that the moral decision each German made then is still, in 1950, burningly alive in the consciousness of every German; and knowing, too, that because sinners and innocents cannot be merged into one there can be no hope for a united Germany.

6

Because this issue is not dead,* it was not only inevitable, it was essential, that the trial for murder of a man called Heinrich Baab should have begun in the city of Frankfurt in March of this year. It was a completely German trial, prepared and conducted by Germans, and it is significant that the man was brought to trial for murder although he was not accused of having, with his own hands, committed murder. It was as if the will of the German people was putting on trial in a German courtroom, before German judges and a German jury, the actual substance of Germany's other reality.

Heinrich Baab was indicted on a charge of participating in fifty-six cases of murder in Frankfurt in the years 1938 to 1943. Other charges included "aiding and abetting in murder, attempted murder, deprivation of liberty, use of coercion to obtain information, and assault and battery." It was reported

---

* Although the preview performance of the Passion Play at Oberammergau on May 18, 1950, was attended by the President and the Chancellor and Cabinet Ministers of the West German Republic, and by the American and British High Commissioners, there has been much German criticism of the actor chosen to play the leading role. Anton Preisinger, who plays the part of Christus, is a former S.A. man, who participated in 1933 in the Nazi raid on the Ettal Monastery in Bavaria. The actor who plays Judas in the Passion Play claims to be the only male member of the cast who was not a Nazi Party member, and his protest against Preisinger being given the role of Christus has been the loudest and most eloquent. Cardinal Faulhaber of Munich was not present at the opening performance of the play, while Alois Hundhammer, the Bavarian Minister of Culture, and a devout Catholic, also failed to attend.

"Sources close to the [Bavarian] ministry," writes the *Neue Zeitung* (Frankfurt edition, May 19, 1950), "expressed the opinion that Dr. Hundhammer's trip to the United States was in the nature of a protest, and that he, as well as Cardinal Faulhaber, who was likewise conspicuous by his absence, were opposed to Preisinger having been cast in the role of Christus."

that, before giving himself up to the authorities, Baab had confidently remarked that none of the people with whom he had had dealings during those five specified years could be expected to appear as witnesses against him, for they were all undoubtedly dead. The first sight I had of him, he was seated in the prisoner's dock, with only his large, balding head and his heavy shoulders visible above the panels of dark, varnished wood. He had a pallid, bloated face, this forty-one-year-old Frankfurt citizen, and he wore a khaki shirt, the collar of which seemed tight around his fleshy neck. His broad rayon tie, which had apparently been striped in yellow and brown in its time, was now faded, and his heavy head, with the front half of the skull naked of hair, hung sideways. For, despite the fact that he was on trial for the murder of fifty-six other Frankfurt citizens, he was concerned with some kind of tidbit, some kind of nut, which his fingers kept shelling out of sight below the panels of the dock. With his head inclined at this angle, the polished area of his broad, flat skull was mercilessly exposed, and his blunt-fingered heavy hand could be seen only at those moments when he contrived to slip a nut into his mouth. As he prepared the next morsel of food for consumption, his sagging jowls went surreptitiously into motion, and his glance moved carefully around the courtroom as he chewed. His slightly bulging, heavily lidded eyes looked slowly and without expression over the occupants of the two benches which seated the press, and over the assemblage of spectators that packed the room, passing the two police officers at the double doors of the public entrance, and the green-uniformed guards at the door used by the press, seeming to seek not a face he knew there, but merely the confirmation that his furtive masticating was not being observed.

8

Upon the entrance of the presiding judge, the two associate judges, and the eight members of the jury, Heinrich Baab rose, as did all the others seated in the courtroom, and one could then see the bull-like, nearly neckless torso in the cheap, shiny, striped wool jacket that could no longer be brought to close across his tightly belted paunch.

The hall in which the trial took place was small—unfortunately, far too small to accommodate the crowds that pressed up the ancient stairs every Monday, Wednesday, and Friday of the four weeks the trial endured, and that waited, hour after hour, for word of the proceedings at the panelled doors. But those who came had no need to come, for they already knew the story well. No member of the local German-American Club, a social and essentially snobbish organization introduced by Military Government for the purpose of improving German-American relations, with branches in every city and town of the zone, reached the courthouse at seven-thirty in the morning to wait at the closed doors for a seat, nor did any member of the Frankfurt Chamber of Commerce; no handsome German cars, driven by chauffeurs in livery, waited outside the courthouse as they wait outside the Bad Homburg casino, or outside de luxe Frankfurt restaurants where one may dine on trout in aspic, and pressed duck and other delicacies, and where the German management reserves the right to refuse service to American enlisted men. Had there been present one or two of those German businessmen who are to be seen every day entering the former I. G. Farben building (now used by the American, British, and French occupation authorities, and known as the Headquarters Building), in well-cut overcoats of imported wool, carrying leather briefcases in their smartly gloved hands, it would have given another meaning to the proceedings, and there might have been reason to believe that the German caste system had indeed begun to go. Not only was there no American in that crowd, but no representative of the West German government in Bonn lent his presence to the chronicling of this new chapter in German legal history. Those who were the spectators at Baab's trial were, in the main, Baab's victims as well. If they were not actually the murdered, they were those whose annihilation had been attempted, or they were of the flesh and blood of those who had died. They were poor, and they were, in many cases, shockingly maimed. Their jaws were askew, their teeth were gone, and, in some instances, the remnants of their shattered faces had been pieced together so that they might once again bear some resemblance to men. There were some without arms among them, and others—and these not necessarily among the aged—whose legs were so crippled that they walked with the aid of canes. There was one young man who sat regularly in a spectator's seat about whom it was later testified that not one thread of his under or outer garments had retained its original color, so drenched were they by his own blood after a visit to Heinrich Baab in 1942.

Of what, and of how many, was this man Baab a representative, this man who was, as were the greatest musicians, a pure product of Germany? For how many had he acted, this man with the heavily lidded eyes, the full cleft chin, and the lips curved with a flourish of vanity and sensuality? For how many did he speak in the years 1938 to 1945? When you put this question to gently bred Germans, they will tell you that Baab was no more representative of Germany than Al Capone was representative of America; and it is possible to concede that there is a resemblance between the two men in the flesh. But there is one factor which must set them apart forever, and that is that Baab functioned as an official, with official sanction, even after the population of Frankfurt knew, either through experience or by rumor, the kind of man he was. For Heinrich Baab was a Gestapo official, and an S.S. trooper, who had been proud of his title "The Terror of the Frankfurt Jews."

On November 21, 1945, in his opening statement at the Nuremberg trials, Justice Robert H. Jackson, Chief of Counsel for the United States, said of the twenty-odd defendants there: "These prisoners are living symbols of racial hatreds, of terrorism and violence, and of the arrogance and cruelty of power. . . . They took from the German people all those dignities and freedoms that we hold natural and inalienable rights in every human being. . . . Against their opponents, including Jews, Catholics, and free labor, the Nazis directed such a campaign of arrogance, brutality, and annihilation as the world has not witnessed since the pre-Christian ages. . . . If these men are the first war leaders of a defeated nation to be prosecuted in the name of the law, they are also the first to be given a chance to plead for their lives in the name of the law." But Baab was a small criminal, and, as the prosecution was to point out in the course of the trial, he attained the status of a big criminal only because his quality was identical with those others whose names had come to be known throughout the world. Baab was not a war leader, and no such "hundreds of tons of official German documents" or captured film as Mr. Justice Jackson referred to in his opening statement at the Palace of Justice in Nuremberg existed in this man's case. The evidence against him had been collected almost entirely from the memories of living German women and men, but the proof was no less valid merely because it resided in nothing more ponderable than their anguished testimony.

A year after Germany's defeat, this S.S. trooper who had eventually achieved the rank of S.S.-*Untersturmführer*, had been released, because of ill health, from a French P.W. camp. He had then joined his family, who had been evacuated during the Allied bombings to the Eastern Zone. There he lived in Thuringia, in the mountains, unable to apply for work in fear of revealing his identity, for it was on record that he had, for a brief time in 1940, worked "in the interests of the Gestapo" in Poland, and he had no desire to face trial in a Communist-controlled court for the crimes he had committed there. It must be supposed that he, even more hungrily than other Germans, read the various reports in the East Zone papers, and gave ear to the many rumors as to what was taking place, in 1947, in the *Spruchkammer* (denazification) courts of the West Zone. He, in company with even smaller Nazis, must have welcomed the intelligence, so widespread throughout Germany, that there had been since 1945 considerable change both in the viewpoint of the population and in the viewpoint of the conquerors—at least in the American Zone, the zone in which Heinrich Baab's interests lay. He must have believed with great readiness, because he wished so to believe, the report that to get employment in this zone it sufficed to show your Nazi credentials to German businessmen. And he must have accepted without question the cynical legend that, in 1947 in the American Zone, all worthy Germans looked upon German anti-Nazis as men who had betrayed their country in her hour of need. To accept all this meant that Baab was secure in his knowledge that he had never dishonored his Party, and he came to believe that only in an East Zone court would there be any consequences to fear. So, late in 1947, upon receiving a summons from the Frankfurt *Spruchkammer* courts, he returned with his wife and his two sons, confident that in submitting to denazification here he would be judged a "follower," * would pay his fine, and then go free. He had not counted on the mass grave opening, and the halt, the blind, and the maimed, emerging from it, for not one of those who had survived annihilation had forgotten either the syllables of Heinrich Baab's name or the features of his face. In February, 1948, before the *Spruchkammer* proceedings got under way, it became evident, through the weight of evidence these many witnesses submitted, that this was not a case to be disposed of by a denazification court, but was indeed a criminal case. Baab was immediately placed under arrest on orders from the district attorney's office and was kept in prison during the two-year period required for the preparation of the case.

To those who read the stories in this book, it may be of service to point out that the courtroom scene described in the story entitled "Aufwiedersehen Abend" is that of a *Spruchkammer* trial, the whole basis and procedure of which differ from the established court procedure followed in the murder trial of Baab. In the *Spruchkammer* trial, there is no jury. The judges and prosecution officers for the *Spruchkammer* trials were originally appointed by the Denazification Branch of American Military Government, and were chosen on the basis of their clean political record and not because of any previous legal training. Whatever subsequent appointments

* The five denazification categories are: major offender, offender, minor offender, follower, and exonerated.

have been made by the German Ministry of Justice, the onus of American protectorship remains in connection with these trials. Thus, in defying the legally untrained Germans who officiate at *Spruchkammer* trials, the defendants, and their experienced counsel, have the satisfaction of feeling that they are, by the same token, defying the authority of the Occupying power. The particular session of the former newspaper editor's trial with which I deal in my story is largely factual. The anti-Nazi editor who testifies to his persecution under Hitler is based on the character of a Catholic journalist who, in company with a group of other liberal German newspapermen, recently spent three months as a guest of our government in the United States. The session described in my story was, unfortunately, the last to be held on this case. Inconclusive though it was, the high feeling of the townspeople against denazification proceedings, and the defense tactics of ridicule, rendered impossible any continuation of the case. The former Nazi editor, the defendant, has now begun publishing a newspaper in a town not far from the one where his paper flourished during the Nazi regime. He has circumvented Occupation regulations by publishing it in his son's name.

With reference to German public sentiment concerning denazification, it is of interest to consider three of the points of a twelve-point program adopted in the autumn of 1949 by the three component groups of a leading right-wing extremist party, formerly known as the *Nationale Rechte,* and now known as the *Deutsche Reichspartei.* The formally adopted program of this party, which is now being organized on a national level, demands that the question of war guilt be decided only after all German documents have been investigated by a German committee, and an international commis-

sion has checked the records of all countries which participated in the war, in order to determine each country's share
of the guilt. It further demands that all denazification activities
be terminated, internment camps abolished, and compensation
be made for unjustified imprisonment under denazification
measures, and that the German government insist on
the establishment, without delay, of an international court for
crimes against humanity. Adherents to the principles set forth
by the *Deutsche Reichspartei* have said to me that all official
representatives and statesmen of countries which recognized,
and had dealings with, Hitler in the postwar years should
forthwith be brought to trial in the international court which
this party has proposed.* It was perhaps the moment, then,
when self-compurgation had reached such fanciful extremes,
that the question of guilt should be settled in a smaller courtroom, among a handful of humble women and men, and that
the case of Heinrich Baab should be accepted as a test case
for them all. Like the twenty-odd defendants at Nuremberg,
Baab was assigned experienced counsel, and was given the
chance to plead in a court of law, not for his life, in this case,
but for his liberty. For the severest penalty permitted for any
crime is hard labor for life, and this was the penalty the
prosecution was to ask.

In the first days of Baab's trial, it was shown that the lives

* Under date line of May 10, U.P. reports that in Flensburg "a Rightist
politician and ex-General Ernst Remer told an enthusiastic audience at
Husum, in south Schleswig, that he could never accept the Nuremberg
verdicts against German war criminals 'until the Allied war criminals
are hanged beside the Germans.' His statement evoked thunderous applause from his four hundred German listeners. Remer, who got a jump
promotion to major general because he smashed the July 20, 1944, plot
against Hitler's life, said he did not regret his action against the plotters."

and the liberty of many hundreds of human beings had passed through this one man's hands. Had he not had the good fortune to be a policeman in a police state, it would be difficult to conceive of him as anything but a bored and belligerent taxi driver, or café waiter, an unwilling servitor with a permanent chip on his shoulder, ready to dispute the amount of the tip one gave him as insolently as he had disputed the right of men and women to live. He could never have become a white-collar worker, for the signs of the requisite patience and industry were missing, and it is doubtful whether his vanity would have permitted him to labor with his hands. It was he who, as the head of Amt II B 2, the *Judenreferat* (the office for The Handling of the Jewish Question), from August, 1942, to June, 1943, had jurisdiction over the disposal of the Frankfurt Jews. (Baab's predecessor in this position, a man named Nellen, committed suicide in 1945.) "The once flourishing Jewish community of Germany," writes Jack Hain in his "Status of Jewish Workers and Employers in Post-War Germany" (Visiting Experts' Series, 1949), "which contributed so greatly to the German economy and its culture, has been reduced from more than 500,000 in 1933 to today's estimated population of 20,000. . . . In Frankfurt, for example, which city before the Nazi regime claimed the second largest Jewish community in Germany,* there are now only 365 German Jewish residents." But, in his foreword to this survey, Leo R. Werts, former Director of Manpower Division of Military Government, points out: "While the brunt of this inhuman attack was borne . . . by German citizens of the Jewish faith, it must be kept in mind that all social organiza-

---

* Over 30,000, according to official records.

tions, whether secular or religious in nature, were persecuted for holding firm to the ideals of equality and brotherhood." By February, 1943, due to the fanatical zeal with which Baab, and his predecessor, performed their task, the last full-blooded Jew had been deported from Frankfurt. But, inasmuch as Baab's duties were not limited to the liquidation of one group of people only, the violated faces of those who watched him from the spectators' seats in the courtroom were not only the faces of Jewish women and men.

Among the one hundred and fifty-seven witnesses who were called to give evidence, there was, for instance, a tall, strongly built, stubborn-jawed young man, with a shock of thick, tan hair, who, neatly dressed in a gabardine raincoat, a gray suit, and well-polished shoes, took his place at the witness table which stood in the arena below the judicial bench. His brown hat lay on the table before him as he sat in the traditional manner, with his back to the spectators, and his stolid, florid, square-browed face raised toward the presiding judge. In accordance with German legal procedure, it was the judge who conducted the examination of the witnesses, but it was the prerogative of the defense counsel, the prosecutors, and also the members of the jury panel, to cross-examine the witness either during the judge's examination or after it had taken place. The sleeves of the witness's gray coat were pulled a little short as he leaned his arms forward on the table, and he posed them there with an awkwardness strange in one who appeared to have an impervious covering of phlegm or nerve beneath his healthy blond skin. But because that armor of phlegm or nerve had been shattered once, he used his strong arms in a singularly helpless, self-conscious manner, as if, for the rest of his life, it would be these arms alone of which he would be aware. For, from the height of the press bench, it could presently be seen that, on the inside of each wrist, the witness bore a deep, disfiguring scar. The story that he told in a low dogged voice was simple enough: in 1939 he had been denounced, possibly by neighbors, as an anti-Nazi who listened to foreign broadcasts. He had subsequently been arrested and taken to Gestapo headquarters at Lindenstrasse 27, a gray stone building that might better have served as library or museum, and that still stands, miraculously untouched by bombs, in the ruined heart of a residential section of the city. The building is now used for the offices of Frankfurt's *Oberbürgermeister,* and there the witness had first been questioned, and then beaten insensible by S.S.-*Oberscharführer* Heinrich Baab. The cellar of Lindenstrasse 27, was partitioned into cells, and the witness had lain in one of these cells for several days, during which time he could hear the screams of other prisoners in the cellar of the house. After several futile attempts, he had eventually managed to reach the light bulb which burned night and day in the ceiling of his cell, and, having broken it, he had sawed at his wrists in the darkness with one of the larger pieces of glass, but had not succeeded in reaching the arteries. When the witness had completed this much of his soberly given testimony, an elderly court physician was called upon to examine the mutilated wrists, and to give a professional opinion on the possible consequences of the act which the witness next described. The day after the suicide attempt, the witness said, Baab had ordered him put in chains, and had then interviewed him again. In response to the presiding judge's attentive questioning, the witness admitted that he was at the time still suffering from the effects of the beating he had received, and was, as well, weakened by

18

the loss of blood. On the pretext of examining the wound,
Baab had disarranged the medical dressing on the witness's
right wrist, and then he had taken an indelible pencil from his
jacket, and run the pointed lead under the bandage and into
the open wound.

"Perhaps blood poisoning will accomplish what you didn't
bring off," Baab's comment was when this was done.

The presiding judge, *Landgerichtsdirektor* Wirtzfeld, who
had served for some time as a juvenile-court judge in Berlin,
gave every evidence of being of a gentle and fastidious nature,
a man of breeding and refinement, with a sharp, sad, patient
face, and graying golden hair. Although almost consistently
throughout the trial his features bore a look of alert forbearance, it was obvious that his heart and soul went sick within
him as the details of this story, and the stories of others,
were told by the men and women who were to sit at the little
table below him in the darkly panelled room. It is to be supposed that he, and his two associate judges in their flowing
black robes and crisp white ties, and the two women and six
men of the jury, had examined the records of the evidence,
for before each of them, as before the prosecutor and his
associate, lay a copy of the forty-six-foolscap-page indictment
(which was twice, during the trial, expanded by additional
evidence). But Wirtzfeld, and the ten other members of the
Court, listened with rapt attention, now and then making
notes, now and then referring to the pages of the indictment,
as the stories were given life by the voices of those who
had, again by some miracle, not died. On one occasion, when
a witness testified that on calling at Lindenstrasse 27 for his
father, whom Baab had questioned, and had found him with
blackened eyes and a broken jaw, one member of the panel,

a plump, competent-looking man, with a bald head and a gray moustache, took off his glasses and spoke out clearly from the bench: "That is true! I saw him!" And there were those among the spectators who could not keep from groaning aloud in horror and protest either at the monstrosity of the thing that was described, or at the memory of what they themselves had once experienced or once seen done to others, which the words of the witness now recalled. On these occasions, Wirtz-feld would raise his hands in the most temperate of gestures, and ask that the spectators help, not hinder, the work the Court had undertaken to do. Mr. Justice Jackson has pointed out in his preface to "The Nuremberg Case" that "the German judges and the legal profession as a whole were among the last of the groups to stand out against the Nazi regime," and whatever proportion of that profession these men of the Court represented, it is certain that they were gravely concerned with the principles of justice and humanity.

It should not, however, be concluded that either the judges, who had been appointed to their positions by the Land Hesse Ministry of Justice, or the jury, whose members had been selected from a permanent jury panel of some several hundred names, had been chosen to sit at Baab's trial because of any expressed predisposition toward people of the Jewish faith, or because of any active prejudice against former police agents of the National Socialist Party. The judges and the prosecution had simply been named to function at whatever criminal trials were scheduled for hearing on the calendar of the Frankfurt assizes during a specified period, and the men and women of the permanent panel are selected by a committee composed of representatives of the leading political parties and trade unions of Hesse. Panel members are chosen for their reliability and their standing in the community, and while the law bars only the first three categories of Nazis from serving on a jury, Dr. Riese, one of the associate judges, told me that he does not recall a former Nazi Party member having served on a Frankfurt jury, at least in the criminal court. It is safe to say that they were, these two women and six men, a valid cross section of the responsible citizenry not only of Frankfurt, but of Germany, and although it would be an error to see them as representative of the majority of the German people, they are representative of a potential majority. The professions of the six men who sat on either side of the three judges, and who were distinguishable from them only because they wore no judicial robes, were given as: an official in the bureau for the restitution of property to Nazi victims, a messenger in the *Oberbürgermeister's* office, two clerks, a mechanic, and an employee of the Frankfurt streetcar company. One of the two women, a plump little woman in her middle fifties, with gray, elaborately curled hair, owns a tobacco shop in Frankfurt, while the other, a slender, dark, worn-faced young woman, is a housewife, and the daughter of Johanna Kirchner,* in whose memory a street in Frankfurt has been named.

With the exception of the chief prosecutor, *Oberstaatsanwalt* Dr. Kosterlitz, a man in his late forties and a Nazi-classified "mongrel" from Berlin, it so happened that no one of Jewish blood officiated in this trial which was one of a number of criminal trials at which the same judges and same panel would, as a body, preside. But the equity and patience of even

---

* Johanna Kirchner, a former secretary of the Social Democratic Party, was in 1942 taken by the Nazis from France, where she had fled before the outbreak of war, and was tried and executed in Frankfurt in 1944.

these diligent members of the Court seemed tried as they listened to the physician explain at length, and in the most tedious terms, and with endless reiteration, the various kinds of blood poisoning which might prove fatal if the hypothetical patient were not treated in time. The doctor was a solid, pink-cheeked little man, with closely cut white hair, and although he expended a great deal of valuable breath in the effort, his voice was so asthmatic that it was not easy to follow the laborious descriptions he insisted on giving of certain diseases which, while not in the remotest way connected with blood poisoning, might likewise, if neglected, produce symptoms of a suppurative nature, and eventual death. It was perhaps not his lengthy monologue, but rather the sight of the cold-eyed defendant who did not cease chewing his surreptitious tidbits in the dock, which caused a young woman in the back of the crowded courtroom to slide, unconscious, from her chair. But the doctor's discourse was thereupon cut short by Wirtzfeld who leaned down from the bench to suggest that the doctor leave the examination of the witness for the moment and attend to the young woman who had been carried out by the court guards.

During the brief time the doctor was absent, another witness was called. This time it was an anxious, angular-boned, slight woman, wearing cheap patent-leather slippers with a strap across the bony instep, who took her place at the table below the judges' bench. She said she was a seamstress by trade, shifting uneasily on the chair as she said it, her voice so deprecatory that it was necessary to lean forward to catch her words. She wore a brown velvet hat on her knot of dark hair, and a beige suit which bore signs of having been cut and recut, lengthened and shortened, and pieced this way and that, time and again, by a seamstress's nimble fingers, in observance of the altering whim of fashion. A brown fur piece, composed of several tired, shabby little beasts, was fastened tightly around her agitated neck, and she spoke now and again with nervous belligerence, as if for a great many years she had been told (and perhaps even recently been warned again) that the things she was saying were not the proper things for a German woman worthy of the name to say. But still she testified that in 1942 Heinrich Baab had arrested her seventy-two-year-old Jewish mother-in-law, and, in the course of events, she had been permitted to go to the Frankfurt station to take the old lady some family photographs and a change of linen before she boarded a train. This train, the witness stated in response to Judge Wirtzfeld's gentle questioning, consisted of several sealed boxcars, in one of which her mother-in-law had left in company with "a great many other Jewish people." She said she believed there were four cars in the convoy, and she thought it possible, she added (as if hearing the far voices of neighbors speaking in rebuke and threat), that these Jewish people believed they were going to be "resettled in the East." Then, two and a half months later, the witness had been notified that her mother-in-law had died in Auschwitz of "natural causes." That was all. It was for another witness to testify that Baab had frequently taken his young son to the Frankfurt station to watch these sealed trains leave.

When the doctor returned to the courtroom, the striking, gray-maned prosecutor, Dr. Kosterlitz, whose lively sense of drama was to add gusto to the theatrical quality of the trial, leaped to his feet in his flowing black robe, adjusted his white tie on his bold, opera-singer's throat, and asked Judge Wirtzfeld for permission to put a question to the medical man. It was granted, and as Kosterlitz drew one quick, strong hand back over his smoothly groomed, abundant hair, he could scarcely contain his impatience, scarcely temper the vehemence in his voice.

"For fifteen minutes," he cried out, "we have listened to your opinion on the effects of diphtheria on the mucous membrane, the effects of tuberculosis on the lungs, and the effects of cerebral meningitis on the brain! I believe you were asked by the Court to give a professional opinion as to the effects that might be produced by the insertion of the point of an indelible pencil into an open wound. Would you be so kind as to answer that question, please?"

In this outburst, it was evident that Kosterlitz was attacking far more than one pedagogue's inability to stick to a point. He was, there could be no doubt, assailing the rigid medieval mold of professional German thought, and the outrageous bombast of official German communication, and doing so out of long and enlightened conviction, knowing more literally than any stranger, who comes upon it only on occasion and can even find humor in it, how it can circumvent action, invalidate knowledge, and trouble the essence of truth. Once Kosterlitz had addressed this question to the elderly doctor, the latter murmured, "I was just coming to that, *Herr Oberstaatsanwalt.*" And there was a note of profound injury in his voice as he stated, in the space of half a minute, that an indelible pencil inserted into an open wound might, under certain circumstances, produce blood poisoning of a serious nature, and that it was probable Baab, as a layman, had believed it would cause the witness's death. Kosterlitz flung himself into his seat again with apparent gratification, and made a written note of the physician's closing statement. Across the arena from him, the defense counsel, a lean, scholastic, Hamlet-visaged young man with horn-rimmed spectacles, sitting in his black robe in what appeared to be a chronic state of sour depression and distaste, also made a note of the physician's statement. The defense counsel had asked only one question of the witness with scarred wrists, and that was as to the width of the bandage and the degree of tightness with which it had been applied to the wrist, a question that contained the obvious implication that a pencil could not have been inserted into the wound if the bandage had been of normal width and had been properly affixed. But he made his note without any perceptible sign of satisfaction, as if aware that if the prosecution failed to prove the charge that the defendant had participated in murder, this evidence of the defendant's intent to kill at least one man might very well be the point on which the validity of the indictment would stand or fall.

It is not to be doubted that Dr. Lengsfeld was in bitter opposition to all that his client had stood for in Nazi Germany. While it is true that Baab had himself engaged Lengsfeld as counsel, he had done so because of his reputation for astuteness, and not for any known past political affiliations. A portion of Lengsfeld's obvious depression could perhaps be attributed to the fact that when Baab's money gave out early in 1950, and he could no longer pay counsel's fees, the Court had promptly reassigned the case to Lengsfeld, who had no choice but to carry on with it, no matter what his personal opinion may have been by that time, and no matter how small the Court stipend might be. During the pretrial selection of jury members from the panel, Lengsfeld insisted that no survivors of concentration camps should be permitted to serve on this particular jury, but it may be presumed that he made this stipulation in no other spirit than respect for the rules of equity. If he lacked the qualities of warmth and eloquence which would have drawn public sympathy to him in this role he had to play, it was evident that he had recourse to rich compensation in the way of fine points of law, and in the complexity of legal interpretations and precedents, that to the mind of the average man and woman, could not but seem as dry as the dust of the ruins outside the courtroom windows. But Kosterlitz was made of other flesh and blood entirely.

Dr. Kosterlitz can perhaps best be described by the French word *fin,* which means that he is subtle and quick of mind, and exact and light of speech; although German, he had acquired, through intelligence, an almost exclusively Gallic fusion of shrewdness and lucidity. There were times when the others officiating in the Court seemed nothing more than effigies in wax, and he the one living man among them; for it could be seen that he was not only the appointed conscience of the state, but likewise the playwright and the producer of this drama in which he played. The son of a Jewish mother, who had died in Auschwitz, he must have known the lines by heart at least fifteen years before he had succeeded in getting the piece upon the boards and the words in the mouths of living players. He had studied law in Breslau and served as a judge in Upper Silesia, before he was forced by the Nazis out of the legal profession in 1933. He then became a clerk in a charity organization in Berlin, but in November, 1938, as the synagogues burned, Kosterlitz was removed from his white-collar job by the Gestapo, and put to work with a road gang, carrying cement and breaking rock. He managed to procure a laborer's job in the Siemens factory in Berlin, and worked

there until 1943, when he was again arrested by the Gestapo
and set to work laying railway ties. Arno Rudert, co-editor
with Karl Gerold of the *Frankfurter Rundschau*, a liberal,
non-party daily, with the largest circulation of any newspaper
in Hesse, said to me recently: "There will be no postponing
and sabotaging of these trials as long as Kosterlitz is prosecutor
here."

It is part of the record that Heinrich Baab came of honest,
working-class people, a class into which, through pre-Hitler
trade-union education, democratic ideology had been pro-
foundly instilled. Baab's father was a tailor, and is said to
have been a member of the Social Democratic Party (S.P.D.),
and Baab, while still in his teens, joined the *Reichsbanner*, a
militant, uniformed branch of the S.P.D. The *Reichsbanner*,
which functioned in violent opposition to the Nazi S.A.,
served principally as a bodyguard to S.P.D. speakers, kept
order at party rallies, and its members derived prestige and
satisfaction from dressing up in quasi-military outfits and
throwing their weight around. This predilection for uniformed violence is not uncommon in the young of many countries, and in the ordinary development of children and events,
it might have led to nothing. Had it not been for the temper
that prevailed in Germany at that time, it is possible that Baab
might have become the industrious locksmith his family had
apprenticed him to be. But, in 1927, when his three-year
apprenticeship was completed, the old urge for command,
for uniformed prestige, possessed him again, and he withdrew
from the trade-union influence and joined the Frankfurt police
force instead of pursuing his trade. At one point during the
trial, Kosterlitz brought up the question of Baab's choice, and
it was shown that it had not been made for material gain. How

much the traits of his character motivated his later decisions, and how much those traits were the result of the hideous pressures of that time, cannot be judged; but it can be said that his eight years of *Volksschule* education, and his three years of apprenticeship, had failed to produce a reasoning, responsible man. Baab, and his early training, must be of vital interest to us, for in the time that Baab functioned as an official he was not an exception to a rule of enlightened and sagacious men, but he, with other men who had received a like training, was of the calibre which an established government vested with greater and greater authority. That training must be of particular concern to us, for it is the same which young Germans receive today.

"The child of a German worker," Alice Hanson Cook wrote in 1947 of the still unimproved educational system in postwar Germany, "still goes to school until he is fourteen years old, and is then apprenticed at a few marks a month, usually for three years, during which time he receives one day's schooling a week in subjects closely related to his trade education. The chief educational influences which play upon him are those inherent in an apprentice relationship to a skilled workman— at best, a paternalism, at worst, three years of enslavement and exploitation." Thus, Mrs. Cook continues, the trade union and the labor party "historically became the educational agencies which influenced the further development of the workers as a rational and cultural being."

Whether Baab knew exploitation or paternalism during the years of his apprenticeship, it is certain that, at the termination of it, any further development for him as a "rational and cultural being" ceased. With panic and menace in the air about him, he made the ignorant and cowardly man's choice for the

police side of the coming police state. Sometime within that
interval, his belligerent fervor for democratic socialism had
turned upon itself and become a belligerent fervor for National Socialism, and in 1932, on the eve of the ruthless Nazi
annihilation of the German trade-union institution, and the
liquidation of its principal leaders in concentration camps,
Baab joined the National Socialist Party "for idealistic reasons." By 1933, he had joined the S.A., and become a *Block-
helfer*, a *Blockwart's* aid in the block-by-block Nazi super-
vision of the urban population, and in 1937, he offered his
services to the Gestapo, not for any increase in authority, he
is on record as saying, but because he had married in 1934 and
now had a wife and child to support. As a Gestapo agent he
received a fifty-mark monthly increase in pay. "Under the
Nazis," Mr. Justice Jackson said in his opening statement at
Nuremberg, "human life had been progressively devalued
until it finally became worth less than a handful of tobacco
—ersatz tobacco." The records of those days show that five
Reichsmark per execution was paid the inmates of concentration camps who were compelled to execute their fellow
prisoners. Polish women were rewarded with a few cigarettes
for inflicting corporal punishment on Russian women, and
Russian women inmates were given the same remuneration
when they were forced to inflict corporal punishment on
Polish women. By 1937 the name "Gestapo" had become
synonymous with "murder," and for fifty marks more a
month Heinrich Baab chose it as the organization in which
he wished to serve. In October of that year, he was put to
work in the *Kirchendezernat*, the church specialist department, with twenty-five agents working under him. "The
Gestapo," Mr. Justice Jackson said in his closing address at

Nuremberg, "appointed 'church specialists' who were in-
structed that the ultimate aim was 'destruction of the con-
fessional churches.' The record is full of specific instances
of the persecution of clergymen, the confiscation of church
property, interference with religious publications, disruption
of religious education, and suppression of religious organi-
zations." In 1938, Baab was promoted to a position in the
Unterabteilung II A, the department for the persecution of
Communists, and by 1940 he was a member of the S.D., the
hard core of the S.S. organization.

Under examination on the first day of the trial, Baab
dropped his unseen bag of nuts long enough to stand up and
state that, in the years which the indictment covered, he had
always worked under the orders of the Frankfurt Gestapo
chief, Oswald Poche (who is believed to be in hiding in the
East Zone). The procedure for sending an offender to concentration camp, or placing him in "protective custody," was
quite simple, Baab further testified as he stood with his two
hands spread heavily on the wood of the dock to support
his body's weight, and his head thrust forward toward the
judicial bench in an attitude of craven anxiety. An oral or a
written denunciation sufficed for arrest, he said, and once an
offender had been questioned at Gestapo headquarters, his
dossier was drawn up and sent to Poche's office where the decision for each individual case was made. The dossiers, ini-
tialled by Poche, were then forwarded to the *Reichssicherheits-
hauptamt* (R.S.H.A.) (Supreme Headquarters of Security of
the Reich) in Berlin where the warrants for arrest were issued.
It was obvious, as Baab addressed the Court, that he had retained an unqualified respect for this man Poche, whom he
spoke of as being "unapproachable" to anyone as lowly placed

as himself; but it was likewise obvious that he had an unqualified respect for the authority of the black-gowned gentlemen who now sat in judgment on him. He gave his answers rapidly, but in an uncertain voice, his two hands holding him upright; for, inasmuch as all conscience and all capacity for distinguishing evil from good had long ago been eradicated from his cognizance by ten years or more of irresponsible action, there was as little coherence left in his mind as there was cohesion in his ailing flesh. One day, the apathy of his being clearly implied, you were told it was the right and proper thing to exterminate the Jews, and other elements of menace to the German state, and the next day you were brought to trial for it. And it is possible that he was honest in his cold, sullen inability to understand how this change of superiors, this abrupt transforming of right into wrong, and wrong into right, had taken place. But if he was honest, then the spectacle of the man himself, and the general conclusion his attitude implies, becomes even more terrible to contemplate.

When he was questioned as to the methods employed to obtain information from those he had arrested, Baab said he had never administered any corporal punishment during the examinations other than "clouts on the ear." At this the entire courtroom, nearly to a man, rose to its feet and cried out its protest, and although he did not then, or at any time during the proceedings, turn his head to look at these people in the courtroom, his fingers could be seen to tighten on the wood of the dock, and in the soft flesh of his right jowl, a pulse began to beat, and his throat quivered for some minutes like the throat of a frog. Not until June, 1942, he continued when the uproar in the courtroom had quieted, did the Berlin headquarters of the R.S.H.A. authorize "rigorous examination," and then it was permitted to bring pressure to bear on those detained. "Rigorous examination," he stated in answer to Judge Wirtzfeld's request for a definition of this term, consisted of administering twenty-five blows with a stick, but Baab added that he himself had taken no part in these beatings. The "rigorous examination" had been conducted in the cellar of Lindenstrasse 27 by two S.S. men who had been "drafted into the service" for this operation. Following this— sometimes as long as three days later, it was to be shown, when those who had been beaten were able to walk again— the detained were brought up to Baab's office for the customary examination, and then, Baab stated, the report on each case was sent to Poche for final disposition. In response to further questions put by the Court, Baab explained that Poche's initials marked in green crayon on the dossier of a case were the authorization for "protective custody," a term which, it developed, meant that the prisoner was placed in concentration camp as well, but merely because it was "necessary to protect him from public violence." In general, those entitled to "protective custody," Baab amplified, were Jews, or other undesirables, who had World War I decorations, or who had lost sons at the front in World War II, or other like considerations. Such offenders were sent to Theresienstadt, in Czecho-Slovakia, which was "considered a great privilege for Jews," Baab said. On March 17, however, a witness gave evidence that prisoners paid Baab and Poche for this privilege. He himself had been a rich man, and he had "sacrificed millions" to buy his and his family's way into this "old-age ghetto" where one was temporarily spared the fate of entering the gas chambers. But "millions" were not necessary, this witness explained, the price for this privilege being, quite simply, all the money one had.

As for those thousands who had been evacuated to Poland, Baab stated that he had never known their fate, because such information was top secret and would not have been divulged to anyone in such a lowly position as his. He said, leaning on the dock still, that he had been ordered by Sprenger (*Gau-leiter* for Hesse, who also committed suicide in 1945) to see that Hesse was "de-Jewed," and that he had, in the process of carrying out this order, organized twelve mass transportations of Frankfurt Jews. These journeys, he said in a low, hurried voice, were like any ordinary journey from one point to another, for the travellers paid their own fares to Poland, and, before leaving, were asked merely to submit a written state-ment of their property to the authorities. In further self-vindication, Baab explained that when Poche demanded that Jewish offenders be sent off on twenty-four hours' notice, Baab had pointed out the impracticability of this, and Jews were thereafter usually accorded three days to wind up their affairs, and were allowed to take fifty marks, and fifty kilos of belongings per person, with them. Apparently Baab con-sidered this a very fair deal.

Before this spectacle of one element of a nation's people brought to trial by another element of that same people, the inevitable and unanswerable question arises as to how strong in Germany each of those elements now is. If this Germany for which Baab stands as symbol can be dismissed as a mere handful of madmen, then does it follow that the members of the Court, and the spectators in it, must likewise be dismissed as a mere handful of sane men who do not speak for the multitudes of Germany? Are the multitudes of Germany something quite different from either of these two groups of which I write? Are they the Germans with whom one talks in shops, and in streetcars, and on the streets every day, and who still will not believe that mass annihilation took place? Whichever the true answer may be, it has been established that the handful of madmen for whom Baab spoke succeeded in exterminating six million people of the Jewish faith, while the handful of sane men and women sitting on the judicial bench speak for an element whose protest was never audibly made. In the spring of 1941, when the repercussions of this great madness swept across frontiers and into France, the Marseille police, under orders from Vichy, stood at every exit of the great railway terminus there. They had orders to check the papers of all those who arrived on the packed trains, and they were looking not only for foreigners of military age (survivors of Dunkirk or others seeking to get through to England) in order to hand them over to the German commission in Marseille, and not alone for criminals, but for Jews of any nationality. The cars which the German Occupation authorities had left to defeated France were ancient and wooden, and the trains were slow-moving, and they ran irregularly, for the main lines were kept open for the movement of goods trains carrying foodstuffs from the unoccupied to the occupied zone. People rode standing in the corridors of these crowded trains, packed even into the lavatories, or rode clinging to the outer steps of the cars. For down to this last rathole left in France came the refugees, the outcasts, seeking a way out—the professors, the lawyers, the doctors, the painters, and authors, and poets of Germany and Austria, with all they possessed in rucksacks on their shoulders, or contained in the suitcases they and their families carried. (And more than one of them bore in grief, in his belongings, a handful of the soil of Germany.) They were halted, these fleeing thousands, and those who were Jews were sent by the Marseille police in truckloads to detainment camps outside the city, where they must wait until they had obtained visas for the countries where they hoped to go. It did not end there; in the night, in that year, the police would enter hotel bedrooms, and ask for the papers of those who slept there, and those who were Jewish, and who had no visa for another country, must dress, and pack their bags again, and were escorted to where the other damned and hunted were held. It was said then that it was not members of the Marseille police force itself who were forced into this work, but special police brought from Vichy, and from the course of history, and the sound of an entire people's protest, it can be said that they spoke for Fascist Vichy, and for no elected French authority.

What, then, had happened to the German mind that it felt then, and has expressed since, so little revulsion for the known anti-Semitic laws as they were enacted and enforced? There is a woman I know, a professor of philology in a Hessian university, who was for a long time loath to talk with me about the fate of the German Jews. And then one night, in 1948, she began abruptly to speak.

"It was a gradual process," she said, seeking to lead me to some understanding of it. "Fifteen years ago, the signs appeared at the entrances to towns, official signs saying *Juden unerwünscht* [Jews Not Wanted]. There was a sign like that on the bridge you can see down there, and others placed at the streets which lead into the town. There was never any protest made about them, and, after a few months, not only we, but even the Jews who lived in the town, walked past without noticing any more that they were there. Does it seem impossible to you that this could have happened to civilized people anywhere? I can only say that we, as you know, are a civilized, cultured people, and that this did happen. And then one November night in 1938, the town synagogue was burned. It was burned by men in civilian clothes, but we never knew who they were. The next day, the Jewish people I knew remained in their houses, and there was no protest made, no delegations called on the *Oberbürgermeister* to speak out against it, and there was not a line about it in our newspaper. In fact, even among ourselves, there was very little said. I was on a streetcar the next day, and as we passed the smoldering ruins of the synagogue, someone in the streetcar said, 'I'm ashamed today that I'm a German,' and, it was a strange thing, but none of us turned to look at the person who had spoken, just as none of us turned to look at the smoking ruins after we had passed. There were certain things it was better not to hear or see. Two nights later, the rounding up of the Jewish population began. One of our Jewish friends came to us after dark and asked to borrow a suitcase, and the following morning, many of us walked down to the station with them, and helped them to carry their parcels and bags. There was one little girl who carried her doll, a very large, magnificent doll, and I've always thought it such a foolish thing for me to remember, but when we heard later that all the things the Jews had carried with them were taken away from them at the next station, which was Kassel, I could think of nothing but the little girl going on without her doll. None of them ever came back," she said. "In the first few months, there were one or two letters from them, sent through the Red Cross to their friends here, and that was all."

To the question as to whether there had been rumors as to what had become of these people, she replied that there had been rumors.

"It was said they were put in work camps, and that many died of privation there," she went on saying. "But we did not ask questions. It seemed better not to know. In 1938, I had some trouble myself, for it was reported that I did not have a picture of Hitler hanging in one of the rooms in my home where I conducted some of my classes. This room was considered university property, and it was required to have a picture of Hitler there. So I finally bought a picture of Hitler, but they had them at various prices, ranging from one Reichsmark and fifty pfennigs to twelve Reichsmarks. I bought one for one Reichsmark and fifty pfennigs," she said. "And then, in 1939, I was asked to take the oath of allegiance to Hitler, and twice I refused to do this. It was my students who persuaded me to do it in the end, for they argued that in taking this oath, which so many anti-Nazis had taken before me, I was committing myself to nothing, and that I could exert more influence as a professor at the university than as an outcast in the town." For a little while she said nothing more, and then she finished the story. "In the place where Hitler's picture used to hang in my room, I now have the picture of a Jew, a Jew called Spinoza. Perhaps you will think that I did this ten years too late, and perhaps you are right in thinking this. Perhaps there was something else we could all of us have done, but we never seemed to find a way to do it, either as individuals or as a group, we never seemed to find a way."

It is the sound, then, of an entire people's protest for which one listens here. A Military Government Opinion Survey conducted in 1949 shows that, in some parts of Germany, anti-Semitism was stronger in 1948 than in 1946. "This survey discloses," writes Jack Hain in his "Status of Jewish Workers and Employers in Post-War Germany," "that young people between the ages of fifteen and nineteen show more anti-Semitism, while less is evinced by those in the age group from forty-two to forty-nine. Trade union members show less than non-members. . . . In Bavaria, where anti-Semitism is most rampant, the Catholic Church has sought to foster friendly relations between Christian and Jewish communities, and the national conference of Christians and Jews working in Germany has made this its sole objective. In addition, there are German laws which seek to prevent discrimination,* although the good will to implement them at this time is often absent."

On the opening day of his trial, Baab divulged that in the

---

* An Associated Press item, under date of May 7, Wiesbaden, reads: "Vigorous prosecution of all anti-Semitism has been ordered by the justice ministry of the West German State of Hesse. There have been numerous anti-Jewish incidents recently, including overturning of Jewish gravestones. Police have blamed all these graveyard incidents on small children, but Justice Minister Erwin Stein declared that parents must be held responsible for their children's acts. He ordered prosecution of parents for neglect of their parental responsibility." In a second A.P. item, dated May 20, Dr. James R. Newman, U.S. Land Commissioner for Hesse, is quoted as pointing out to the Minister-President of Hesse that "of five hundred Jewish cemeteries in Hesse, two hundred have been desecrated." Urging the Minister-President to "take every possible step to stamp out the remaining vestiges of racial prejudice," Newman said: "Nothing will do more damage to Germany's standing before the civilized nations of the world than the continued manifestation that racial prejudice and hatred are still alive and active and that these crimes continue to go unpunished."

case of Jews no denunciations or accusations were required. Frankfurt Gestapo agents, he said, were dispatched to the Jewish quarter of the city, and the residents were rounded up and taken to the marketplace. There, a functionary from the Ministry of Finance assisted while these people were searched, and their valuables removed from them. The functionary then made out an official receipt for the rings, brooches, watches, etc., that had been collected, and gave this receipt to the head of each family. Everything, Baab said, was done in the most orderly way, and at this Kosterlitz got to his feet and asked a question of him. Each time the prosecutor spoke, a sense of impatient and vigorous life seemed to waken in the courtroom, and now a high wind of emotion rose among the spectators as he asked Baab if it were true that when mothers herded in the marketplace had asked him in desperation what was to become of their children, he had answered: "Don't worry about those Jewish bastards. You'll soon be on your way up the chimney, and your troubles will be over."

"I was an idealist in my profession," Baab replied to this, his hands supporting the weight of his body still, his head thrust forward from his shoulders, his eyes bulging at the prosecutor from under their heavy lids. "If I used such expressions as 'Jewish bastard' or 'Jewish sow' it simply meant that this official language had become so much a part of my flesh and blood that I saw nothing unusual in it. I never used anything but spiritual weapons in dealing with offenders."

At the time when such expressions were an accepted part of the official language of Germany, the Jews of Frankfurt were liable to sentence of death if they walked in the public parks, or entered a movie theatre, or sat down in a streetcar.

Those who had not been rounded up and disposed of must tread lightly, for to smoke in the street, or present an identity card upside down to an official, was sufficient for a Jew to be taken for examination to the building in Lindenstrasse which had come to be known as the House of Tears. One of these who had not trod lightly enough was a storekeeper who had been seventy per cent disabled in World War I, and whose offense was that he had either failed, or refused, to mark his military citation documents, and his papers of honorable discharge from the German Army, with the word "Israel." It was he who took his place at the witness table now. He was an emotional man, in his late fifties, rawboned, eagle-beaked, stoop-shouldered, and deaf, who appeared as outraged by the fact that Baab had not fought at the front as he was by the atrocities which Baab had committed at home, and who turned in the witness chair to fling his accusations at Baab not only in the name of humanity, but in the name of the beloved Fatherland as well.

And there were others. There was a tall, reticent, doe-eyed insurance salesman whose father had been the director of a Frankfurt insurance company. He sat nervously on the edge of the witness chair, his hat and briefcase on the table before him, swallowing the shyness and modesty in his lean throat as he said that his father had been subjected, on Baab's orders, to "rigorous examination" in the cellar of the House of Tears. His father had subsequently been sent to Auschwitz, he testified, and then he opened his briefcase with shaking fingers, and took out with care the two last letters his father had written him from there. They were dated 1942, and their edges were worn, and their folds had been re-enforced with strips of transparent paper. The insurance salesman's hands did not cease shaking as he read to the Court, in a trembling but clear voice, these final paragraphs. In one letter his father had written:

"I have firm confidence in the justice and mercy of the German authorities."

One of the German authorities at that time was a small-boned, well-groomed little woman called Hannah Reitsch, who had dinner with me on a summer evening in 1948. She had been a test pilot for the Luftwaffe, and had, in the final phase of the war, specialized in testing jet-propelled planes. As she drank a martini in the cool of the evening, and looked down across the river valley, she talked of these test flights, giving a strange, an undefinable other meaning to the things she had done, until it seemed in the end that it had been neither for country, nor leader, nor party, that she had so daringly and fearlessly flown, but for that "obscure, evolving, crepuscular, damp, and shrouded" love which Nietzsche speaks of as mirroring the German soul.* She had had a bad crash in one of the jet-propelled planes, and her neat face bore scars where the flesh had been expertly repaired. She talked quickly, with efficiency and graciousness, of the dreams she had dreamed all through the war of saving human life.

"It was the young I cared about," she said. "I used to lie awake at night, telling myself in desperation, 'Hannah, Hannah, you must find the way! They must not die!' I believed

---

* "The German soul has passages and galleries in it, there are caves and hiding places, and dungeons therein; its disorder has much of the charm of the mysterious; the German is well-acquainted with the bypaths to chaos. And as everything loves its symbol, so the German loves the clouds and all that is obscure, evolving, crepuscular, damp, and shrouded; it seems to him that everything uncertain, undeveloped, self-displacing, and growing is 'deep.'" *Beyond Good and Evil*, Nietzsche.

41

that as a woman I had failed, and, above all, as a flying woman I had failed, if I could not find the way for our planes to cut through the cables of the London barrage balloons. Every night our young pilots, our bomber crews were dying, dying uselessly, senselessly, because their planes would enter the area of these balloons and fall. I was just completing an invention, a system of knifelike blades in an advance position on the planes which would be strong enough to sever the cables, and then the jet-propelled missiles were perfected by our scientists! I think I began sleeping at night then when I knew those young men need no longer fly straight to their deaths," she said, and she looked at me with bright, transfigured eyes.

We had shrimps for dinner, and she called them "little crabs," and laughed about them. It was a long time since she had eaten "little crabs," she said. She was working with the expellees from the East Zone, and she said that those she knew were destitute and hungry.

"Now it has become my mission to work with them, to dedicate myself to these homeless people who will never, as long as they draw breath, relinquish their love for their soil and their homes," she said; and after drinking a glass of white wine with the shrimps, she spoke of April 20, 1945. "It was Hitler's last birthday," she said, "and I was in the last German plane to make a landing in Berlin." She had flown in with Field Marshal Greim, who was to take over command of the Luftwaffe, for Goering had by then turned traitor and begun negotiations with the Allies, and Greim had been summoned to Berlin to take his place. From the night of the twentieth until the twenty-seventh, she had remained in the Reich Chancellery bunker in company with Hitler, Eva Braun, Goebbels and his family, Bormann, S.S. General Fegelein, and a few others who had rallied to the *Führer's* side. "There were moving hours during those final days," Hannah Reitsch said, speaking quickly, softly. "Toward the end, Fegelein and Martin Bormann turned on their friends and left. But Fegelein was captured, and, on Hitler's orders, was executed by his own men. On the twenty-seventh, Hitler ordered Greim and me to fly to the southeastern army and air command to rally all forces to the defense of Berlin. We accomplished the first part of our mission, that is, we managed to take off from the airfield, and we were the last German plane to take off from Berlin, and we got as far as Austria. There our gas ran out, and we made a crash landing. Greim committed suicide when the Americans seized us there."

She was eager to speak of these things, and she listened with interest to the things one said, but she did not wish to speak of, or hear of, the fate of the German Jews. She took a little drink of wine, and she said:

"You see, I was a flying woman, a birdwoman, I only knew what was taking place in the sky. I was not even a member of the Nazi Party, for I scarcely knew what the whole thing was about. If you belong to the air, you do not know what is taking place on earth. How can you know?" While she talked, her small hand dropped on my arm from time to time, and she spoke of love, of that tremendous love which women, above all, must possess to overflowing for humanity. "You have it, just as I have it," she said. "Love and pride. You will understand what I mean when I tell you that I could never work with the Americans, no matter how much love I might have for them, and no matter how much value my experience as a jet pilot might be to them. My pride tells me, 'no, Hannah, you cannot do this. You would be betraying those German flying men, those birdmen, who had faith in you.' But there are Americans who had faith in me, too—Americans in New York," she said, and she smiled as her fingers touched my arm. "I went there before the war, and it is indescribable, the ovation I had! On East 86th Street, near Third Avenue, I think it was, there is a fine big hall, and I still have the clippings describing my reception there. It was in a part of New York called Yorkville, where a great many fine Americans live, and the hall was decorated with German and American flags, draped on the platform and hanging from the ceiling to the floor. It was one of the greatest nights of my life. Hundreds who had come to hear me speak had to be turned away at the doors, and when I came out on the platform, the crowds in the hall went mad! In one great voice they called my name out for a quarter of an hour without stopping for breath, and I tell you, the tears were streaming down my face when I began to speak. In fact," she said, and she gave an unsteady laugh, "I couldn't speak. I just had to stand there with my arms held open to them, to these people of your country who understood the great love I had for everyone, and who gave me their love and their faith in return." She lifted her glass, and the tears were standing in her eyes now as she took another swallow of wine. "As things are now, I cannot put foot on an airfield, can't even touch the wing tip of a plane," she said. "This is not easy for one who belongs to the sky. But every time I see a plane going over, any plane, my heart goes with it, and I know that I shall fly again."

During the time that the various witnesses gave evidence in the courtroom, the restless vitality of Kosterlitz never knew surcease. He made rapid notes, ripped open letters which were borne across the arena to him by a green-and-black-uniformed court guard (a man with black waxed moustaches, and a long shaved head topped by a narrow black brush of hair, who bore a startling resemblance to Kaiser Wilhelm II in his prime, but whose manner was as gentle with the shabbily dressed who constantly sought entry, as to the men who sat in their black judicial robes and whom he approached softly, on his toes). Once Kosterlitz had scribbled his answers in a firm hand across these letters, he would beckon the guard to take them for dispatch, or he would make notes on the foolscap pages of the indictment. At times he snapped his fingers for a glass of water which, his classical-featured operatic head flung back, he would down in a single draught. It was manifest in every gesture he made that he was impatient to play his role, but he was not idle as he waited in the wings. There were moments when he appeared to be working in restless fury on corrections of the original script, for, indeed, nothing had been forgotten in the drama which unfolded. Even humor was provided in the form of testimony of an ex-Gestapo *Kriminalrat* (a high official in the criminal section) who, during those same years, had worked under Poche in an office adjacent to Baab's.

The *Kriminalrat*, whose denazification proceedings are still pending in the British Zone, was the perfect cartoon figure of the Teutonic man. He was poker-spined, his narrow skull was shaved, and there were sabre scars across his cheeks. Even seated in the witness chair, he did not remove the light-colored, belted raincoat that, in common with knee-high boots, is a predilection of the Nazi-minded, and that in his case, was nearly identical to the raincoat Hitler habitually wore. The *Kriminalrat* was obviously a man of better education

45

than the prisoner in the dock, and to the questions put him by Judge Wirtzfeld, he replied in a quiet, low-pitched voice, and only after some moments of deliberation. In answer to one of these questions, he stated, with a certain wariness, that he had always believed that various courses in citizenship, and other instructive subjects, were given the inmates of concentration camps. In fact, he had been under the impression, he said, that the initial purpose of these camps was to instruct those who were lacking in an understanding of their duties to the state, and he intimated that nothing that had developed since had given him any reason to change his mind. When the ensuing laughter of the spectators had subsided, Kosterlitz, standing tall and statesmanlike in his black robe, fixed the *Kriminalrat* from under his lively black brows, and asked him if he had at any time during the ten years from 1933 to 1943 heard rumors as to the extermination of human beings being practiced in these camps.

The lapses of memory which the witness suffered were not infrequent, and this was one of the occasions on which he repeated the question slowly and carefully, as if striving to get the sense of it, but in reality altering its outer shape and its inner essence, so that no sense was left to it at all. "Extermination" was, in the end, the only word of the original question that remained, and as he said it, in slow puzzlement, he might have been using it with reference to vermin, but to what species of vermin he had not yet been able to make out. At this, Kosterlitz's voice sounded in warning:

"I must remind you that you are required to speak the truth here. Did you or did you not hear any rumors as to what disposition was being made of the inmates of these camps?" The *Kriminalrat* was then able to recall that "at a very late date"

46

he had heard some sort of rumor. "At what date?" Kosterlitz asked.

"Oh, late. Some time toward the end of the war," the *Kriminalrat* answered after consideration, but Kosterlitz was not done.

"Would you say you heard that rumor before 1944, or later than that?" Kosterlitz asked, and, after a moment's reflection, the *Kriminalrat* ventured the guess that he had heard it some time in 1944. "And from whom did you hear the rumor?" Kosterlitz persisted. The *Kriminalrat* sought to avoid answering this question by, in measured words, referring to his concept of his legal rights. He did not see the necessity of answering this particular question, he said. "Indeed," said Kosterlitz, his voice light and clear, "you are required to answer any questions concerning this public matter that the state puts to you in this public courtroom, and you are required to answer such questions truthfully."

The *Kriminalrat* thereupon conceded that he believed it was a woman who had made mention of the rumor to him.

"And who was this woman?" asked Kosterlitz.

"A friend," said the *Kriminalrat*, speaking even these two words with the greatest care.

In reply to Kosterlitz's next questions, he said he did not recall the woman's name, or the name of the street, or the number of the house in which she had made the remark to him.

"What rumor did she repeat to you?" Kosterlitz asked then, but the *Kriminalrat* said he had forgotten the details of the conversation, and therefore could not say. "Did she speak of the Jews being sent to extermination centers?" Kosterlitz proceeded with it, and, after some moments of hesitation, the

Kriminalrat said that he believed she had said something about Jews dying in the camps where they had been sent for re-education. "Is it not possible that she, knowing your position, asked you if it were not true that Jews were being exterminated?" Kosterlitz suggested, and the *Kriminalrat* replied that he could not recall the exact words she had used, but it was possible that she had asked him in that way. "Did she use the word 'gassed'?" Kosterlitz said, his voice gone soft and winning, as if to charm the truth from him. But the *Kriminalrat* was being extremely wary. He said he did not recall that word being used. "What, at the time, was your reaction to what this friend repeated to you?" Kosterlitz asked.

"I told her not to mention such things again," said the *Kriminalrat*, choosing his words with care. "It was my duty to turn a person in who repeated stories of that kind, but, because of the circumstances, I did not do so. I was convinced that she had been misinformed. I myself," he added, "when I heard of the mass deportations to Lublin, was under the impression that the Jews were to be resettled there."

The testimony of this cautious man must have been of some comfort to the prisoner in the dock, and, as he listened, the mask of apathy seemed to shift a little on his features, but no richer, sweeter emotion was revealed beneath. He, who had protested that the witnesses had all been influenced in their testimony against him, sat motionless, unmunching, a faint wash of life seemingly restored to his face as he heard this witness state that the Gestapo had never been the all-powerful organization which everyone had been led to believe it was. The Gestapo had been grossly misrepresented, the *Kriminalrat* said in his stolid, deliberate way. Gestapo agents had been merely members of a police force that had attempted to keep order. Kosterlitz then put the question lightly and gracefully to him as to why, then, everyone in Germany, if not in all of Western Europe, had stood in such dread of the Gestapo, and had lived in fear of being summoned by the Gestapo for questioning. This, the witness replied, he was at a total loss to understand.

"The procedure was," he said, "that if it seemed advisable at any time to bring pressure to bear on an offender in order to obtain information essential to the safety of the state, an application for permission to bring pressure had first to be forwarded to the R.S.H.A. in Berlin. To my certain knowledge, on one occasion only was such permission requested by Frankfurt Gestapo headquarters, and it was not granted by the R.S.H.A." This was humor of so stark and uproarious a kind that the spectators rocked on their chairs with the violence of their laughter, their mouths stretched open, their hands striking their thighs.

But it must have been smaller comfort to the prisoner when the *Kriminalrat* went on to say that Heinrich Baab had always shown great willingness in executing the orders of his superiors, and had enjoyed the reputation of being particularly "strenuous" in his interrogation of offenders. And word by word now, the truth at which the *Kriminalrat* thus hinted became clearer, and it seemed plausible that, faced with the super-conscientious work of a subordinate whose zeal might even bring him to the denunciation of his superiors, neither the *Kriminalrat* nor Poche had dared show themselves less violent than Baab in their persecution of the enemies of the state. (For instance, it was later shown that the witness who had cut his wrists after being examined by Baab had eventually been acquitted by the district court of Kassel of the charge of having listened to the foreign radio. And it was also shown that even after Baab's transfer from the Frankfurt *Judenreferat* he had persecuted "mongrels" although the official policy was to defer decision on their status until after the war.) The *Kriminalrat* testified that in 1943 he himself had seen that Baab was removed from the *Judenreferat* and put to work in an anti-sabotage division—a piece of information which he volunteered doubtless with his coming denazification trial in mind, and apparently in the belief that it made him appear the more benign agent of the two. But he failed to add that by February of that year, Baab had already accompanied the last convoy of full-blooded Jews to the Frankfurt station and seen them into the assembled boxcars, so that there was, in reality, no further need for him in the *Judenreferat*.

There are those to whom fact is not fact unless it has been transmuted by lyricism. This is just one facet of that genteel and confused intelligence that judges persecution and extermination to be less grave matters when storekeepers and insurance salesmen are concerned than when the victims are people of intellectual distinction. (A Nazi-classified "mongrel," a lady of breeding, said to me recently: "Of course, if you had ever had anything to do with Polish Jews you would understand how the Nazis felt. They were an uneducated, grasping people, not at all like the cultivated German Jews.") The protagonist for all those who make distinctions came to the witness chair in the gentle person of a Frankfurt Jewish author, a man of seventy-two, whose wife had been "Aryan." He sat at ease before the Court, with the light from the high windows touching his olive-skinned face and his soft white hair, not for an instant the long-haired artist out of place in the company of common men, but a man whose voice and manner, whose disciplined emotions and conservative dress, gave him the air of being an academician, an honored man of letters, who now addressed fellow members of honor in this judicial hall. He told the Court that in 1942 he had been arrested by the Gestapo and confined in a "Jewish home" in Frankfurt. This so-called home was, he explained in his quiet, cultivated voice, a mass quarters, or ghetto, where Jews were held pending final disposition of their cases. There he worked with the others at dyeing shoes, sorting potatoes, and performing similar tasks.

"I must speak first of the inner grandeur with which the people confined there accepted their fate which was, almost without exception, death," he said. "They were the living figures in a frieze of such beauty, and of such noble, heroic character that replicas of it should be painted upon the walls of every public building of the new Germany. There are no words in any language of the civilized world to describe the suffering the Jews endured at that time."

One of the first occasions on which this distinguished man of letters had seen Baab was when Baab paid a routine visit to the "home." While passing through a workshop, the witness's grave and precise testimony went, Baab had remarked in his presence: "When I put in an appearance, it means some corpses are due."

"After Baab's visit to the ghetto, a tide of terror and anguish seemed to sweep through the place," the witness said. "The weakest became panic-stricken, and were submerged by it, while the strongest held their heads higher, as do the drowning, in an effort to outride the flood of fear." On the evening following a visit by Baab, an elderly woman hanged herself, the witness told the Court. She had been very musical, and in her luxurious home there had been two concert grand pianos, each placed so that the musician at the keyboard could look out upon the lawns and gardens as he played. She and her married daughter had spent three hours every day at one or both of these pianos, playing for each other, or playing duets, or playing arrangements for two pianos. During her confinement in the ghetto, the old lady had talked to the witness of reports made by students who had had themselves hanged by the neck for a certain period, in the interest of research, so that they might record the sensations experienced. And the reports, she had told him, were that, after the first deafening explosions, the ears of the hanging were filled with music of such incredible power and beauty that they were regretful, resentful even, when they were cut down and must return to life again. "I like to believe that she died to the sound of that music," the witness said. "It had been arranged," he continued, "that her daughter and son-in-law should walk past her prison window every night at seven o'clock, so that she might know that all was well with them. This they had done with unfailing punctuality during the six months she was there. But on this particular evening she waited in the greatest agitation until twenty minutes past the hour, and when they did not come, she concluded that they too had been arrested by Baab, and she took her life at the very moment that they passed." After an instant of silence, the witness proceeded: "My bed neighbor during those months was the former director of the Stuttgart Alliance Insurance Company, a gentleman of wealth and prominence who was then nearly seventy years old. On one of Baab's visits of inspection, he accused this eminent man of 'sabotaging the *Führer's* work' by not dyeing enough shoes per day, and he was forthwith removed to Auschwitz, where he died. I cannot tell you of the eternal loneliness which entered my soul the night he was taken from the home. It was not only that the bed beside mine was left temporarily empty of life, and in particular of the life of one I had known well, but for the first time I saw, wide and dimensional before me, the actual vista of each man's solitude, so vast, so terrible, so silent, that I knew this window which had opened upon it was one I could never again close. Baab," said the witness, speaking without anger or bitterness, "knew that every person he sent to Auschwitz faced death. He was a mass murderer. When he summoned men and women to Lindenstrasse 27, the murder had already begun."

Witnesses came and went in a steady procession to and from the witness chair—witnesses who testified that they had been beaten by Baab, and the teeth knocked from their mouths, witnesses who had been threatened by Baab with reprisals on their relatives if they did not inform, other witnesses who had survived the so-called ghetto who had heard Baab say to the guards: "The Jews will be taken to Auschwitz, where they will be gassed." There was one witness whose Jewish wife, after being interrogated by Baab, hanged herself in a cell in Lindenstrasse 27; another who had lost eighteen members of her family in the deportations from Frankfurt; others who had seen Baab knock down an old Jewish lady at the Frankfurt station; another who testified that Baab had sent the Jewish wife of a Frankfurt bank director to her death in Auschwitz because she had gone to an "Aryan" hairdresser; another, the mother of seven children, whose husband had been arrested by Baab with the words: "This is separation for life," and who testified that Baab had returned for the children, on the pretext of letting them visit their father, and she had never seen any of them again. When one witness testified that he, and therefore presumably others in Germany, had known as early as 1941 that concentration camp inmates were being liquidated, people even outside the courtroom, could they have heard, must have stopped to listen. Postal orders sent to friends and relatives in the Lodz ghetto in Poland had been returned, he said, with the official notification stamped on them that the addressee had left without giving a forwarding address, and this was as final as if a death certificate had come. At the conclusion of each witness's testimony, Judge Wirtzfeld read out the name of the witness, his street address in Frankfurt, and the date on which he had come into contact with Baab. And each time this was done, Baab ceased chewing his surreptitious tidbits, and got to his feet again, and, with his hands gripping the wood of the dock, faced the two women and nine men of the Court. Each time his response to Judge Wirtzfeld's question was the same. With no inflection in his voice, and no apparent interest in his own words, Baab would repeat:

"The name is familiar, but I do not remember having seen the person before."

This obstinacy in denying that he had ever seen witnesses whose faces he had struck, or witnesses who had been to his office not once but half a dozen times to ask for news of relatives whom he had "detained," caused such outbursts of protest among the spectators that Baab, his face drained colorless, and his bloated throat beating like that of a frog, asked in accordance with Article 20 of the Hesse Constitution, for the protection of the Court. But the recitation, and the subsequent publication in the local press, of the names and addresses of the witnesses, had its effect upon the people of the city. Not from one source, but from many—from shop employees who served one from behind a counter, from taxi drivers, from postmen, or from the man or woman who happened to sit next to one on a park bench—came the incredible admission that for the first time, now that names and addresses had been given, statistics had ceased to be statistics and had been translated into flesh and blood. The Nuremberg trials were far removed, not only in time but in comprehension, for no little people had appeared as witnesses against those who had once been the great. For the first time, with the names and addresses of commonplace citizens crowding the scene, many in Frankfurt came finally to believe that vast numbers of other commonplace citizens, with names and addresses as commonplace as theirs, had, in the Nazi years, been systematically and deliberately destroyed. The photographs of the massed naked dead that were shown to the Germans in 1945 had been dismissed by most of them as propaganda photographs, for the general belief in Germany is that anything may be resorted to in the dissemination of propaganda, inasmuch as propaganda is merely one means of putting over a discreditable cause. "The Nazis did it for twelve years, and now the Americans and the Russians are outdoing each other at it," the Germans say with cynicism; but the sworn testimony of men and women who lived in the same streets in which they lived, or just around the corner from them, shocked and convinced them as no reports had done before. Here a Herr Georg Wittmann, living at Laundhardstrasse 1, in Frankfurt-am-Main, had told of things he had actually seen done, and a Herr Peter Meister, Thorwaldsenstrasse 20, had given similar testimony; and here was a Frau Grete Hoffman, a Jewess married to an "Aryan," living as anyone else might live at Wilhelm-Buschstrasse 24, who had endured years of slave labor because she had omitted the Jewish name Sarah from her ration card. Here, then, was the testimony of simple, honest Germans like themselves, who had nothing to gain by telling a lie.

The great majority of letters received at the *Frankfurter Rundschau* offices on the subject of the Baab trial expressed deep sympathy for the members of the victims' families, denounced Gestapo methods, and were violent in their condemnation of Heinrich Baab. Some correspondents even went so far as to demand that special legislation be passed in order that Baab might pay with his life for the crimes he had committed. Among these letters there was, however, a sprinkling of anonymous communications, some scribbled in pencil on postcards, expressing regret that Baab had not been the instrument for killing more Jews while he was about it, and among them the editors of the *Frankfurter Rundschau* (who, incidentally, are not Jews). But these latter communications were in no way representative of the public's reaction to the trial. Fear was frequently voiced by irate citizens that the defendant might be acquitted on a legal technicality, for no member of the Gestapo had, in West Germany, been convicted of so much as participation in murder for the functions he had fulfilled.*

* On March 16, 1950, at the height of the proceedings of the Baab trial a verdict of "not guilty" was returned in the trial of two former *Kriminalräte*, who had been tried in the Hamburg Criminal Court for having used "coercion to obtain statements" from prisoners during the Nazi regime. In his justification of the verdict, the presiding judge pointed out that "in every state means of coercion must be allowed the police," and that it had "not been proved that the defendants had abused the authorized means."

On March 23, 1950, in the Munich Criminal Court, the former S.S. Gestapo Chief of Munich, and his deputy, were both found "not guilty"

But, day after day, as the persecuted and the dead took on
their separate identities, the man in the dock, in the same measure, became less and less man and more and more the detached
inhuman symbol of the criminal organization he had served.
So that the incident which took place in the courtroom on
March 13 was startling to those who had long since ceased
speculating on Baab's role as husband, or father, or son, and
who could hardly conceive of him in any surroundings more
personalized or intimate than those in which they saw him
now. On the morning of that day, one witness testified as to
the treatment which his mother had suffered at the hands of
Baab in 1942. She was then over seventy, the witness told the
Court, but despite her age, and her delicate health, Baab, during his interrogation, had struck her so forcefully with his
fist that she had been knocked the length of his office by the
blow.

"I saw her only once after that," the witness said. "The following week she was deported to the East, and she died in
the boxcar on the way. But this I did not know at the time.
When I went to Lindenstrasse to beg Baab for news of her,
I asked him, in the name of pity, if he did not have a mother of
his own somewhere—"

---

of responsibility "in the execution without trial of at least twenty eastern
slave laborers and Polish deportees," or of "aiding and abetting in man-
slaughter," or of "inflicting grave bodily injury" on the numerous prisoners who had been in their charge. Although the two defendants had
admitted in Court that they had requested the R.S.H.A. for permission
to hang ten slave laborers, and that twenty-five to forty executions had
taken place in the cellar of the Gestapo headquarters in Munich, the jury
failed to find the defendants guilty on all counts.

In the latter instance, the prosecutor has appealed the verdict, and
the case will come up for retrial.

"Yes!" a voice cried out from among the spectators. "And there she is!"

Immediately, two women dressed in black, one young and fresh-cheeked, the other old and squat, and as bloated as the prisoner in the dock, rose quickly from their chairs at one side of the crowded room and, with lowered heads, hastened in panic toward the door. There the uniformed court guard, with his waxed moustaches and his black brush of hair, stepped forward on tiptoe to open it for them, and the men and women in the courtroom sat in shocked silence, watching Baab's mother and wife, who had so inexplicably, and only for this brief instant, taken shape before them, bow their heads and go.

On the sixth day of the trial, another former Nazi official took the witness chair.

Dr. Kurt Lindow, a man in his middle forties, had been director of the Criminal Section of R.S.H.A., in which position he had worked with Admiral Canaris. In contrast to the *Kriminalrat*, Dr. Lindow was obviously a man of superior intelligence and education, and he was not, it may be noted in passing, one of those to whom it might be said, as Mr. Benjamin Buttenweiser, Assistant United States High Commissioner for Germany, said of the Germans in a recent address: * "Father, forgive them, for they know not what they do"; nor was Dr. Lindow one whom one might hope (to draw again on the text of Mr. Buttenweiser's speech) "to lead hand in hand along the pathways to a better life." Dr. Lindow's life had

---

* This speech, scheduled to be delivered on May 14, 1950, in Chicago at the annual meeting of the Anti-Defamation League of the B'nai B'rith, was cancelled by a committee of the League because of the sentiments regarding denazification which Mr. Buttenweiser expressed. The speech was later given in New York before the Foreign Policy Association.

been, in fact, not a bad life at all. Both before and during the war, he had travelled widely abroad in a diplomatic capacity, representing Nazi interests at international conferences. His oval face was tanned, his dark hair immaculately groomed, and the gray felt hat he carried, his gray topcoat, his white shirt, his black shoes, were impeccable. Since the war he had appeared as a witness in two of the Nuremberg war crime trials, and he had had his own *Spruchkammer* trial in Darmstadt in 1948. In his *Spruchkammer* trial, Dr. Lindow had been classified an "offender" (a member of the second category of Nazis), and sentenced to three and a half years at hard labor, a sentence that had been considered served because of his internment by the Americans since 1945. Dr. Lindow's manner was quiet and assured, for his experiences for the most part had been not disagreeable ones, and neither he, nor anyone else in the courtroom, with the exception of Kosterlitz, anticipated for an instant the *coup de théâtre* which was about to alter the tenor of his life for an undetermined time to come.

Dr. Lindow had been summoned to appear in the Baab case in order to testify on the functioning of the R.S.H.A., but a detailed exposition such as was asked, he stated in response to Judge Wirtzfeld's questioning, he found extremely difficult to give. The implication was that he himself had operated on such a high level that he scarcely knew what went on below, and he further reminded the Court that everything connected with the matter had taken place a good many years before, added to which, the duties of the bureau had been complex and multiple. When Lengsfeld asked him if, in the routine reports forwarded from subsidiary Gestapo bureaus to the R.S.H.A., it had been customary for the reporting Gestapo agent (Baab or whoever it might be) to make a specific suggestion about the disposition of the individual reported on, and, if so, whether the R.S.H.A. acted upon these suggestions, Dr. Lindow replied that matters of this nature had not come to his attention. He was, however, able and willing to explain the meaning of the term "protective custody." Protective custody, he said, was a measure which had been introduced "to protect from persecution individuals who had been under suspicion or arrest." For instance, if an individual had been tried and cleared by the People's Court, the Gestapo had the right to step in with a "staying order" on the ground that one who had been accused or suspected of an offense might be considered a "threat to the security of the state" and therefore required official "protection" (and one could only assume this meant protection from his neighbors and friends). On being asked what he had known of the means employed to dispose of the Jews, Dr. Lindow replied that when he saw no more people in the streets wearing the Star of David, he had concluded the Jews had all been resettled in Eastern ghettos, and had given the matter no further thought. And now the high point of the session approached.

Dr. Lindow, as it happened, was the hundred and fifty-second witness to be heard, and his undramatic testimony was given not in the morning, but in mid-afternoon, so that attention and emotion were temporarily depleted by the time he took the chair. It was therefore in keeping with the general spirit of exhaustion that Kosterlitz, when asked by Judge Wirtzfeld if he wished to question the witness, waived this right with a presumably fatigued motion of his hand. There was nothing to indicate then that the records of Dr. Lindow's *Spruchkammer* trial in Darmstadt were lying open on the table underneath that hand. Judge Wirtzfeld requested Dr. Lindow to take a seat for the moment on the bench which stood at all times before the spectators, and which was reserved for the overflow of the press and for witnesses who had already testified. Dr. Lindow waited courteously while Kosterlitz put one question to Judge Wirtzfeld in an easy, conversational tone. If the defense had no further interest in questioning the witness, could not Dr. Lindow be immediately dismissed, he asked. Judge Wirtzfeld turned toward the defense counsel, and put his question to him with his eyebrows, and, across the arena, Lengsfeld nodded in sour agreement, not brooding over any objection, it may be supposed, but irked by the life sentence he was himself condemned to serve, perhaps by his digestive organs, in a solitary confinement of wormwood and gall.

"Very well," said Judge Wirtzfeld, seemingly about to yawn. "The witness is dismissed."

And then the three things happened simultaneously. The faces of the spectators turned wearily toward the door, awaiting the entry of the next witness to be called; Dr. Lindow rose from his chair, and, immaculate gray felt hat in hand, began his bow in the direction of the Court before taking leave; and Kosterlitz jumped to his feet and called out in a voice that roused the courtroom from its sleep:

"*Herr Wachtmeister*, place Herr Lindow under arrest! I accuse him of defying all international and human law by murdering Soviet P.W.s in his care!"

The police officer so addressed made his way to Dr. Lindow, and requested him to follow him from the room. Dr. Lindow completed his bow to the judicial bench with dignity, and, with two men in plain clothes falling into step on either side of him, he walked toward the door. Some members of the press hastened from the courtroom, and made their way down the hall beside him and his escort, and followed up the stairs. And here, as he climbed, his composure left him. The color drained from his face, and with each step he took and breath he drew, he sobbed like an aged man. When a member of the press speculated on his being extradited to Russia for trial, this one hundred and fifty-second witness covered his face with his hands, leaned against the soiled plaster wall for strength, and groaned aloud.

". . . whether the [American] denazification program was handled intelligently and effectively or, as some believe, incapably and too complacently, I think it must be agreed that it is too late now to turn the clock back and reopen the entire question," Mr. Buttenweiser also stated in the address to which I have previously referred. "Any such move, I feel certain," he continued, "would produce chaos which would render impossible the performance of the more constructive and far-reaching program of reorientation which lies before us and on which I fervently believe we are already successfully embarked." Kosterlitz, however, did not hesitate "to turn the clock back," needing no program of reorientation to tell him that it is a question that has never been closed. Dr. Lindow is at present in the city jail awaiting trial in the Frankfurt Criminal Court, a trial which may take six months to prepare.

On March 27, Heinrich Baab, accompanied by the members of the Court, and representatives of the press, made a visit to the House of Tears. And here the fleshy, pouch-eyed, balding man could be seen in all his mediocrity. His apathy was dispelled, and he was visibly shaken as he passed through the doorway, stricken and trembling before his memories of the dead as he had not been before the living who had testified against him from the witness chair. He gave a cursory glance at the office which had once been his, not crossing the threshold of it; and he confirmed with a nod of his head that this one, adjacent to it, had been the *Kriminalrat's* office, and this other had been the office of the Gestapo chief, Poche. Then he led the way to the cellar, showing his familiarity with the place in sullen pride. Letters had been produced in Court telling still more stories of the sufferings which those who had written them had once endured here—letters from Pittsburgh, Pennsylvania; Portland, Oregon; Cheyenne, Wyoming; letters from Amsterdam, and Brussels, from those who had survived. And the walls of the cells bore further testimony, for the despairing had scratched words of appeal upon the stone. There were single words, or phrases, in German, in Polish, in Hebrew, in Russian. "Mama!" "Papa!" had been scratched in desperation there, in several tongues, and the dates of various years recorded beneath them. The most recent message was written in French, and it was dated March 2, 1945.

"I have been freed," it said, "but I shall return for those who are still here."

There was the cell where a Jewish woman, a Swiss before her marriage to a Frankfurt Catholic, had hanged herself; in another, two men had taken their lives. And, like a surly museum guide who, despite long association with the wonders that he shows, has remained in total ignorance of their inestimable beauty and their inestimable worth, Baab conducted his visitors through dark winding corridors to a windowless cell, scarcely larger than a clothes closet, which was supplied with air by a small rusty pipe that pierced the outer wall. Here, he stated without emotion, the authorized "rigorous examinations" had taken place. Stooping in the doorway of this cell, Kosterlitz asked him in what position the prisoners had been beaten, and Baab replied that he had never assisted at an examination, and therefore did not know.

"I am not guilty of the death of these people," Baab said in the darkness of the crypt. "During my time of service with the Gestapo, my actions were all within legal bounds, and were performed on the orders of my superiors."

From this place, Baab was returned to the Frankfurt jail where, ten years before, with Gestapo headquarters overflowing, he had conducted many of his interrogations. And there the group of men and women paused with him at the head of a flight of steep iron stairs, and looked down the length of it in silence. Evidence had been produced in Court that Baab had once stood here with a Jewish woman he had finished questioning, and, seeing the hysterical state to which despair had reduced her, said:

"Others have thrown themselves down here and put an end to it. There's nothing to keep you from doing the same."

The day following this trip to Lindenstrasse 27, Baab gave a *Frankfurter Rundschau* reporter a list of twenty-six names of Frankfurt citizens who, he declared, had worked as informers for the Gestapo during his service there. Two of the names on the list proved to be the names of two of the three members from Hesse of the present *Bundestag* at Bonn, while a third name was that of a Frankfurt city magistrate. Although the *Rundschau's* publication of this fact—but not the names —aroused a degree of public interest and protest, and incurred the expulsion from the Social Democratic Party of Karl Gerold, co-editor of the *Rundschau*, Baab's act of divulging the twenty-six names revealed more of the nature of the man

himself than it did of the questionable character of those holding public office in Germany today. For it was easy enough
to establish that many detained by the Gestapo had not infre-
quently been released on parole on a signed promise, which
they had no intention of keeping, that they would inform
upon their neighbors and friends. At least one of the *Bundestag*
members from Hesse (all three of whom were S.P.D.) stated
publicly that this had been the consideration on which he had
been accorded amnesty by Baab.

On the twenty-ninth of March the prosecution presented its
summarizing argument, and the dusty stairs leading to the
courtroom were even more packed, the crowds who waited
outside the guarded doorways even greater, even more eager,
but no less patient, than before. The light of the spring day
came through a long window behind Kosterlitz as he stood
erect before his table, which was so close to the upper press
bench that those who sat there could have counted the stitches
of the neat patch in the back of his long gown. But this shabby
garment that he wore was expendable, for what endowed him
with dignity was his trenchant awareness that six million men
and women and children had had to die before he could be
given this role to play. As he spoke, he held a small black
automatic pencil in his right hand, and when he did not speak
directly to the judicial bench, or to the defendant in the dock,
his eyes would seek this pencil out, and dwell on it, and a portion of his exhortations were made to it, as if it were a frag-
ment of the actual charred flake of Plievier's individual man.
"How heavy is the guilt?" Plievier wrote in 1948 in Germany.
"Can guilt be weighed? How can it be weighed? Children
shot, women shot, old men, helpless prisoners shot—according
to orders, 'as the law provides.' What sort of law? Is it a law

65

of nature, of reason, of metaphysics, of human intercourse? Is it a law dedicated to the preserving of the interests of all? Is it the law of the German people, the same people who brought forth a Gutenberg, a Matthias Grünewald, a Martin Luther, a Beethoven, an Immanuel Kant? Is it the law of a creative people living by the fruits of its own creations? Did the German people have no other political face to show the world?"

It was this political face which Kosterlitz defined the features of in the first hour of his address. As he talked the defendant was forgotten, for it was clearly the principles, and the acts of an entire society of men of which the prosecutor spoke. On the table before him, stacked one upon the other, were three unwieldy tomes of Nazi statutes, with markers set in various pages of them, and now and again he would seize up one of these volumes and read aloud from the contemptible text. Here were expounded in legal terms the reasons why a certain portion of the population must wear the Star of David, and must, according to sex, include the name "Sarah" or "Israel" on all identity documents, or else be subject to arrest. Here was set forth the July, 1935, Citizen Law, with its thirteen supplementary regulations, defining the nature, as well as the civil status of a Jew, and specifying the congenital moral and physical deficiencies that automatically excluded every Jew from the right to citizenship. And here were the paragraphs of a law, passed in July, 1943, which brought the police courts of Germany under Gestapo jurisdiction, so that every avenue of appeal was closed. After Kosterlitz had read one of these passages out, he flung the volume from him, and then he spoke of the Gestapo regulations that had not been written into any law books, but that had been enforced as inexorably as those set forth in pompous official language for the eye of posterity. In accordance with these minor regulations, Jews had been permitted to go shopping once a week, but even on that one day the items they might buy had been rigidly controlled. They were permitted to buy one turnip a week, for instance, and any infringement of this regulation meant arrest. Germans whose ration cards bore the letter "J" were not allowed to buy white bread, or eggs, or butter, or any other luxury items; nor were they permitted to read newspapers, have a telephone or a radio, or enter a theatre or any other place of entertainment, but, at the same time, they were required to pay a theatre and movie tax for productions they were not permitted to see.

"While it is true," said Kosterlitz, coming to the vital point of Baab's personal responsibility in the matter of his victims' deaths, "that the warrants for arrest were not signed by the defendant, but by Heydrich and Kaltenbrunner, it has been proved beyond any doubt that Baab could always be counted on to produce the evidence which the R.S.H.A. considered justified arrest." And then he spoke of two Frankfurt Jews whom Baab was reported to have saved. In this instance, "saved" meant merely that he had interrogated two Jews and, for some obscure reason, allowed them to go free. "This," Kosterlitz cried out, "this alone, is indisputable proof that the power of life and death resided in the hands of Heinrich Baab!"

In one of Carl Zuckmayer's plays, a Luftwaffe general is appealed to by his former mistress to intercede on behalf of a Jewish friend who faces extermination in a concentration camp. And, sitting there, well-groomed and handsome on the stage, the general gazes bitterly out across the audience and, in speaking some of the best lines in the play, voices a profound comment upon the unhappy people of Germany. "Now let us look into the mirror and dote on ourselves!" Zuckmayer makes him say. "What noble human beings we are! That's how we look! Each of us with a Jew or two to salvage his conscience so that we can sleep at night!" Can this, then, be taken as explanation of why Baab had allowed one Jew, of all the Jews who had been summoned to his office, to walk in the streets of Frankfurt with no Star of David on his coat, and had allowed a second Jew to pack his bags and go? It would be too easy to answer that these two Jews had paid Baab for the favors he granted them, Kosterlitz cried out, for what of the other Jews who had paid Baab all the money they possessed, and still they and their families had died? One of the two whom Baab had spared had remained in Frankfurt, and he had told the Court that he was unable to explain why Baab had conceded him the "special favors" that he had. He denied, under oath, Baab's statement that he had informed Baab of a secret meeting hall where the Jews gathered for religious services after the demolishing of the synagogue.

"I could not have told him this, for I was incapable of uttering a word in his presence," this witness said. "Although he treated me with consideration, I always entered Lindenstrasse 27 in fear and trembling, my limbs shaking, my throat dry with terror, for the sound of his shouting filled the entire house."

If he had spared the lives of two, said Kosterlitz, then the power of decision had been his, and the Court had no choice but to find him guilty of the murders with which he was charged.

"This man," said Kosterlitz, concluding his five-hour address, "should be judged as a component part of the furious anti-Semitic program of those years. In passing judgment on him, you take upon yourselves the high honor of passing judgment upon an element and an epoch of Germany."

During Kosterlitz's argument, the defendant sat, heavy and motionless, in the dock, his eyes seemingly drugged, watching the prosecutor with the same lassitude with which he might, on a languid spring afternoon, have watched a voluble street-corner vendor demonstrating a new kind of glue for mending broken crockery, or a new gadget for sharpening used razor blades, or a magical fluid for sealing together the fragments of a shattered looking glass. It was obviously a proceeding which he connected in no way with himself. Inasmuch as he possessed no broken crockery or used blades, and would not have recognized his own likeness in the glass even if it were held before him, he would have preferred to saunter on down the avenue and pick up another bag of peanuts somewhere, and stand looking at something else while he peeled the shells mechanically away. Johanna Kirchner's daughter, who served on the jury, and who, being an S.P.D. member of long standing, had likewise been imprisoned in the Nazi days, had her own explanation for Baab's air of nearly complete detachment from the proceedings of his murder trial.

" 'Do whatever you wish with me' was his attitude," she said to me some days after the verdict had been pronounced. "He believed that any sentence passed on him would soon be meaningless. With more and more Nazis being reinstated in positions of authority every day, he knew he had nothing to fear. He simply sat there thinking: 'Do your worst. I'll be out in a short time anyway.' "

During the weeks of the trial, a young green-uniformed

court guard had sat at times at the end of the bench on which the defense counsel sat below the prisoner in the dock, and at other times had stood at the doors of the press entrance, and, because of the composed earnestness and intelligence of his young face, one's eyes repeatedly sought him out. When one glanced from the defendant's countenance to his, it was as if one turned from darkness to light, from the opacity and muteness of death to the clarity and eloquence of life. On the day of the prosecutor's address, the young guard was not on duty, but he sat, in civilian clothes, among the spectators, and it was apparent that, on his day off, he had chosen to come back and follow what was taking place.

On March 31, Dr. Lengsfeld made the defense summation, basing his argument, with pained and scholarly conviction, on the absence of conclusive proof. Standing with his sour, sallow face raised, his great horn-rimmed spectacles saddling his nose, and his lean arms crossed within the folds of his full black sleeves, he cited a verdict of the Nuremberg Tribunal that held that the Gestapo had had, as an organization, no connection with the operation of concentration camps. The prosecution had not only failed to produce a single arrest warrant bearing Baab's signature, he said, but it had failed to prove that the reports sent to the R.S.H.A. were in any way tantamount to verdicts. Neither had it been proved, Lengsfeld continued, that Baab himself had assaulted his prisoners; and, at this, the sound of protest and laughter rose in the Court.

"Quiet, please!" Judge Wirtzfeld called in admonishment from the bench. "Every man has the right to speak freely here!"

All the evidence produced during the trial showed, said Lengsfeld, that Baab had done no more than carry out to the letter the official regulations issued by the R.S.H.A. If justice were to be done, he said, Baab could not be held responsible for a system that others had set up. Baab had been in charge of one small section of a demagogic state which had been dedicated, in its entirety, to violence; he had been merely one link in an endless chain which had held captive many innocent men and women, he said. Was there, moreover, a legal precedent for the conviction the prosecution demanded, Lengsfeld asked; and he cited the Hamburg Criminal Court's acquittal verdict of March 16, a fortnight before, and the acquittal verdict returned by the Munich Criminal Court at an even more recent date (see footnote, page 56).

"No *Kriminalsekretär* in the Western Zone has yet been convicted of murder," Lengsfeld said. "This fact cannot be lightly put aside. If Baab knew, as has been charged, of the ultimate fate of his victims, then he might be guilty of contributing to murder, but no evidence has been produced to uphold either this or the murder charge. One witness has stated that Baab would find no defense before a divine court, but it must be borne in mind that Baab is not being tried at this time before a divine court, or is he being tried before a political court, but he is being tried before a criminal court, and it is neither divine law, nor political law, but criminal law which must, in all justice, be observed." As the defendant listened, his face seemed to alter, and the features of it appeared for a moment to be moved by a faint flicker of life, a life to which the name of hope might almost be allowed. "It is still to be proven," said Lengsfeld, the taste of the words seemingly as bitter as gall upon his tongue, "that Baab himself raised his hand against any individual," and the protest of the spectators was roared aloud.

At the conclusion of his three-hour plea, Lengsfeld asked

that the defendant be found morally but not legally guilty of the crimes with which he was charged. "No one," he said, "can, from the standpoint of morality, acquit him of his guilt. Deplorable as it may be that both the evidence and the proof that might establish a truer picture of events are lacking, Baab cannot be found guilty as a murderer." He concluded with an exhortation to the Court "to apply the law in its purest and strictest sense and not to be swayed by the pressure of public demand."

On the fifth of April, the day the verdict was to be returned, the young court guard with the steadfast face, and the other, with the waxed moustaches and the black broom of hair, who patterned himself on Kaiser Wilhelm II, stood in their green uniforms at the press entrance, to keep the unauthorized from making their way in. It was a quarter past nine when Baab took his seat in the dock. Almost immediately after he had done so, a middle-aged woman, carrying a black umbrella and wearing a black felt hat, rose from among the spectators, and walked across the Court arena to the vacant defense bench. With her umbrella lifted as a weapon, she flung herself at the defendant in the dock.

"You murderer! You murderer!" she cried, and her voice seemed to be pressed tight and small within her throat by grief.

As she sought to strike Baab's head, he retired quickly to the back of the dock, and the young guard sprang in between. He put one arm around the woman and led her back to her seat, and, when the umbrella slipped from her grasp, he picked it up from the boards and stood it carefully beside her chair, and then left her crying into her hands. Just before Judge Wirtzfeld stood to read the verdict and the sentence, the two guards did a singular thing. They opened one half of the press door wide enough to let first one, and then another, and finally a total of six scrubwomen, hatless and wearing their soiled aprons, slip in and stand among the others who had waited since seven in the morning for the doors to open, and who were packed into the courtroom now to hear the few words that were about to be said.

Although "guilty" was not the first word of the rendering of the verdict, it was the first word those present heard, and a sigh, scarcely more audible than that of water rising and falling along a shore, passed through the courtroom. "Guilty," said Judge Wirtzfeld, and, as Baab stood with his hands supporting him on the dock, he seemed, for a moment, to lose control of the muscles of his eyes. It was as if an invisible, impersonal hand had without warning severed the rope of living fibre that held his eyeballs in their place, and, as he heard the sentence read, they drifted, unmoored, and without destination, in his heavy skull.

Heinrich Baab was found guilty of fifty-five counts of murder, on twenty-one counts of attempted murder, on thirty counts of assault and battery while holding office, combined with six counts of employing coercion, on five separate counts of employing coercion, and on twenty-two counts of deprivation of liberty. He was sentenced to hard labor for life, the loss of all civic rights, and the costs of the trial to be borne by him, save for four charges (one of murder, and three of attempted murder) on which he had been acquitted for lack of conclusive evidence. And, as Judge Wirtzfeld proceeded to deliver his two-hour justification address, in which he deplored that the criminal in the dock should have been of German nationality, the face of the young court guard could be seen for an instant turned toward the press bench, as clear as light with vindicated pride, before it was lost among the faces of the crowd.

The stories in this book do not proceed from the sight of one young man's face in a courtroom. They are, on the contrary, the record of that painstaking search through time and emotion which led eventually to a court of justice. They are the introduction to the trial. For here, in a trial which involved, in its essence, every German, whether he were in or out of Germany, was defined in unmistakable terms the pattern for a revolution which has not taken place, the outline for action which might spring not from an outraged national honor, but from the outrage of a deeper, wider honor. Here was offered the vocabulary for that concerted protest which has through history remained so alien, so repugnant even, to the people of Germany—the protest which wells from a wronged and broken but still wildly beating heart. Yet even Judge Wirtzfeld in his justification address expressed his regret that Baab should have been not a foreigner but a citizen of Germany. One of my great friends, a German writer, a refugee, wrote me last week from New York: "The consequences of our failure as a nation are manifest in practically every individual. We Germans have never fought on the barricades for freedom . . . we have never tried and condemned one of our own kings, or presidents, or leaders. We have never liberated ourselves." Here, in a criminal court, was the nucleus of revolution offered, and the offer made not on foreign, but on German terms.

How many Germans are ready to accept the obligation of those "German terms"? An official in the Frankfurt city administration said to me a few days ago: "The Nuremberg trials were a highly proper proceeding in all except one respect: there should have been German judges as well on the bench." The stage to be prepared by others, was his solution, then, as the union of Western nations is now being prepared by others, with German figures called in for the finale, although, until the last act of both productions, they had been outspoken critics of the plot, the libretto, and the score. How many who are not officials, and who have neither realization of guilt nor knowledge of guilt (as those Germans of whom I write in the story "The Lovers of Gain"), could be brought to accept a national responsibility? They dwell on their separate islands of pain, each waiting for a hand to reach to him, for the word of explanation to be given, the inductive word of love to be pronounced in a language they can understand. For them there is no hope, no life, no self-liberation possible; they are the black flakes "spewed up out of the flames."

In this collection of stories, there is one about a Wehrmacht soldier. On the basis of the evidence this story, "Cabaret," submits he might be taken for a self-liberated German, but "there are caves and hiding places and dungeons" within the German soul. Although he put on a skit which derided both Hitler and Goebbels with such vigor that it assuaged by humor a portion of the German conscience, in another program of this political cabaret, the Wehrmacht soldier played another part. He gave himself the role of an American Military Government officer, and when the curtain parted he could be seen seated with his feet on his desk, chewing gum and reading a copy of *The Stars and Stripes,* while his German secretary, wearing American nylons, and her nails varnished blood-red, handed out employment blanks to former high-ranking, and now destitute, Wehrmacht officers who sought employment tending furnaces, or doing other menial tasks, in the homes of American Occupation personnel. The situation was comprehensible, the repartee plausible, but the uproarious denouement came when a former Wehrmacht general, standing in rags before the gum-chewing American, recognized this official as a former German citizen.

"Mein Gott, I knew you in Berlin!" the man in rags cried. "Your name is Blumenfeld, and you got out in 1933!"

"Wa-a-al, now it's 1948, and my name's Flowerfield, get it?" the American official answered, and the spectators at the *Weinstube* tables rocked with delight.

I discussed this skit with the Wehrmacht soldier, and he said if the use of a Jewish name seemed distasteful, he would change it to something else, but he could not see how anyone could object to it. Such humor was a far cry from the spirit which had destroyed the lives of men in gas chambers, he said to me one evening over wine. Five minutes of humor at the expense of a refugee could scarcely prepare the way for murder. But he changed the name of the American official to Hochstrasse, and then the audience saw nothing funny in the skit, and it was dropped from the program of the cabaret. And my friend in New York, who was once a German himself, would have answered: "Until there has been a national upheaval, a cleaning of our house by our own hands, the twilight will remain."

Frankfurt, Germany
July, 1950

Begin Again

THE AUTOBAHN that runs through Hesse was built for conquest, as were the rest of Hitler's highroads. And, having been built for conquest, it bypasses as it goes all that is humble, simple—the irrelevancy of a barn roof, a silo, a pasture—all that is expressive of the daily life of man. But now this purpose it once had is lost, and the Autobahn serves to link one agglomeration of ruins with another—Kassel with Frankfurt, Frankfurt with Darmstadt, Darmstadt with Mannheim, Mannheim with Karlsruhe, Karlsruhe with Munich—and the Fords, the Pontiacs, the Studebakers, the Plymouths, the Chevrolets stream swiftly along it, and mingled with these and the American Army trucks and jeeps there is German traffic passing as well. There are Volkswagens, with the hard, bisected shells of cockroaches, and prewar Opels and Mercedeses, and high, ancient German trucks that run laboriously on wood combustion, or that leave a volume of dark-brown smoke and a stench behind them, the effluvium of burning Diesel oil.

But there are other travellers on the Autobahn—those with rucksacks on their backs, or string-tied valises in their hands, who wait by the roadside or halt under the bridges, giving a sudden human meaning to the long bleak stretches, setting individual landmarks in the monumental monotony. They will signal the German traffic first, and if the German trucks or cars do not slow down, they will make their tentative gestures to the Americans, even to an American woman driving past. And if you stop, the Autobahn becomes something else; it becomes a conduit for the voices of many people, each speaking the name of his destination and the names of the things that have brought him this far.

There was, for instance, the medical student hitchhiking his way back to his university town. He was a sharp-faced young man, as wary as a cat, who spoke at once of the travelling he had done while he was still a child. He had visited Venice, Capri, Paris, Nice, he said, and he might have been proffering his calling card to the American woman who had stopped to take him in, so that she could rub her thumb across it and find it was not printed but engraved. As he spoke, his thin lips withdrew in pain, distaste, from the words he uttered—English so precisely spoken that it seemed a rebuke to those who spoke it with familiarity.

"We were forced into an unfortunate role," he said, and his long, fleshless hands clung to the handle of his briefcase, that emblem of the cultured, the professionally élite, that only *Herr Doktors* and *Herr Professors* are authorized to bear. "Members

78

of a large family are required to share the blame when one or two of their relatives become criminals," he said. "But to those of us who had acquired another perspective through travel, through study, the whole thing was absurd. In Venice, on Capri, the respect for one order took on its proper proportion."

"That was perhaps 1936 or 1937?" the American woman asked.

"Yes," said the student. "Before anything definitive had occurred."

"When German tourists travelled through Italy with pink tickets to pay their hotel bills instead of money—the arrangement Mussolini made to pay for German coal?"

"I spent two weeks with my family in Florence at that time," the student said, choosing to ignore the question. "My father was a connoisseur of the arts. I shall remember those two weeks all my life," he said, his voice excluding all others from the vision, from the historical and cultural aura of the scholar's dream. "The palaces, the bridges, the museums there —I knew them all."

"They are destroyed now. Some of the palaces; all of the bridges, except one."

"Even you regret that, have a feeling of guilt," the student said. "I respect you for it. Most Americans cannot bring themselves to admit that the Allied bombings—"

"That was not Allied bombings," the woman said. "That was demolition the Germans did."

The student turned his head carefully to look at the woman behind the wheel, and his thin lips smiled. "But why should they have done that?" he said, as if speaking to a child. "What reason would the German military have had for destroying artistic monuments?"

And there was the blond girl in the G.I. overcoat dyed green, with her face painted high and Post Exchange nylons on her heavy German legs. A piece of rope was tied around her suitcase, which had seen so much use it was losing its veneer of leather and turning back into cardboard. She told the American woman she was trying to get to Wetzlar, and she picked the suitcase up by the rope and lifted it in onto the seat.

"My boy friend got Z.I.'d," she said in a nearly perfect imitation of the American tongue, and she closed the door beside her and jerked her short skirt down across her knees. There was the smell of perfume in her clothes still, going stale, and blood-red varnish was splitting from her long, soiled nails. "I been up to Bremerhaven seein' him off. He's a good kid," she said.

"You've learned English very well."

"I ought to," the girl said, "after three years workin' with the M.P.s. I'll be nineteen next week. I got time to look around. I can find me another boy friend if things ain't so easy back home as he thinks they're goin' to be."

"Easy?" the American woman asked.

"He's got a wife, see," the blond girl said, "and she don't know nothin' about me. He's goin' to sack her if he can, but maybe she'll get tough. She's no good. She's holdin' on to him for what she can get. They live in Missouri. It's a real nice place to live," she said.

"Maybe you can find a boy friend who hasn't got a wife," the woman said.

"Oh, it ain't not findin' a boy friend that ever worried me," the blond girl said, and she took a comb out of her cracked leather bag and jerked the dirt-caked teeth of it through the dry ends of her hair. "It's waitin' for the right one to come along, like that Italian girl who didn't have no money either, waitin' for Tyrone Power, like she did. I seen she got fifty new dresses. Only, I never had much luck. I had a girl friend once and she stole all my clothes. Some girls are false, and she sure was false. Like a German fella I knew workin' for the Americans. He wanted to take me out, see, and he didn't have the dough. So what's he do but take some dough the M.P.s left in their pants when they send them to the cleaning plant. Then what's he do but put it onto me, and I'm kicked out! That's the kind of people the Germans are. Don't talk to me about the Germans. They're false friends. Every German was false I ever knew."

The American woman watched the blond girl as she put lipstick on her mouth, watched the sullen, bewildered mask, the blank flesh on which had been painted brightly and viciously a child's stubborn despair.

"You're too young to have your hair all dry and broken like that," the American woman said to her then. "You oughtn't to put that bleach on it."

"Sure," said the girl. "That's what my boy friend says. He says, 'You leave that stuff alone. You're an ashes blond, so don't try to make it no different,' he says. So now I stopped it. My mother don't like it neither. She's in the British Zone. I ain't seen her for two years now. She don't like the Americans. She's a funny kind of a German."

"So your people aren't in Wetzlar?" the woman asked.

"Oh, I'll find my people O.K. Maybe you got a piece of gum on you?" she said. She took the paper from the stick of gum the woman gave her and dropped the paper on the rubber floor mat of the car, between her high, worn heels. "Only,

I won't have nothin' to do with niggers," she said. "I don't know how a white girl can go out with a nigger. They're just like animals. They ain't like men. They sure ruin every place they go."

"No, you're wrong," the American woman said. "They're like the rest of us—some good, some bad."

The blond girl looked up from the sight of her face in the pocket mirror she held, and her eyes went blank. "Excuse me, but I don't understand your English very well," she said.

And there was the young man on crutches, who flapped after the car like a great wild bird as it slowed down to take him in. One leg was gone, just below the hip, and the trouser leg of it ended there, but he used the crutches with such skill, such ease, that they seemed a part of his own articulated bone. He swung himself onto the front seat of the car and laid the crutches out of sight behind, and he dropped his shabby rucksack on the floor against his broken, warped-soled shoe. He brought a singular quality of affection into the car with him; it was there in his mere presence, before he spoke. His destination was Heidelberg, he said, speaking a slow, broad German, and he turned his face in shyness and pleasure toward the American woman as he said the name. She offered him a cigarette.

"My wife and my two children are there," he said, and he smiled at the cigarette with love as he took it and put it in his mouth. He might have been anything—a P.W. returning from France or Russia, or an East Zone expellee.

"How long since you've seen them?" the woman asked.

"Four days," the one-legged man said, and he took photographs from his pocket and showed them, one by one, to the woman. "This is my wife," he said. Her eyes were large, and

82

they seemed to be asking for many things, perhaps even for health, in her delicate face. Her light, soft hair was worn in braids above her docile brow. "She was a Norwegian girl. I married her there, in 1943," the one-legged man said. "Those were the good years—1943, 1944. There was more than you could eat up there—milk, butter, eggs, for everyone—no war, no fighting. Those were good years for everyone," he said, and he put his wife's yearning eyes away.

Those were the years when the gas chambers burned the brightest, the American woman thought, and she glanced at the photographs of the one-legged man's white-haired children as she drove. He had just been up to Giessen, the German, to be fitted to an artificial leg; there was a big artificial-limb works there, he said, where they fitted dozens of war veterans a day. His leg would be ready in a week, and they would send it to him, with directions on how to use it, he said, and so great and simple was his pleasure that the radiance of it seemed to be flooding through the car. Even if he couldn't walk with it right away, he would be able to stand up with it, he said, and if he could stand, he could get a job in the Heidelberg mirror factory.

"I've been waiting three years for the authorization to get a leg," he said, speaking eagerly, happily. "The paper came last week, and I made my way up to Giessen, and a funny thing happened to me there. A man with one arm gone came into the room where you wait to be fitted, and he walked right over to me. 'How have things gone with you since February, 1945?' he said. I was certain I knew his face. I didn't know where I'd seen him before, but I had that feeling you sometimes have that he was someone I had once known well. 'Breslau,' he said to me then. 'We lay next to each other in the field hospital for fifteen hours before they began amputating. The night you lost your leg, I lost my arm,' he said, and we both started laughing. Each of us had enough on him to pay the other a glass of wine, and we went out and drank Moselle together. It was like finding your best friend! I tell you, that one glass of Moselle made me drunk, it tasted so good!" And he began to laugh at the memory of two drunk men, one with an arm gone and the other without a leg, sitting there talking about one night when they had not died. "It's a good thing to get drunk like that sometimes," he said. "You forget about how things are for a little while. My wife has tuberculosis now, and she wants to go back to Norway to see her people there, and leave the children with them, before she dies. 'Now, how do you expect to get to Norway,' I say to her every day, 'if you just sit coughing hour after hour in a chair?' " In the end, he took an apple from his rucksack, and he gave it to the American woman. "They are not as good this year as the apples of 1943 or 1944," he said.

And there was one man who had not set out with the idea of asking for a ride, for he had been driving his own Mercedes when the back axle snapped in two. He could not bring himself to lift his hand to the cars that passed, but he stood by the side of the road with his arms folded, jerking his chin in the direction that he wanted to go. He was a man of fifty or more, small-skulled and as vindictive as an eagle, with an eagle's cold, belligerent eye.

"I have to get to Darmstadt," he said when the American woman stopped, and the language was German, his own, without grace or compromise, hard, nasal, high. "There's a garage there that can take care of my car," he said, and he settled himself stiffly on the cushions of this alien seat. He was riding

here not because this car was better than his own but because
no choice had been left him. His Mercedes had given him
years of service both before and during the war, he said; it
was merely circumstances that had brought about its failure
now. "I believe it is the custom in America to trade your car
in at the end of a year," he said, and the profile rode against
the flowing landscape, beaked like a bird's, the mouth warped
by the acid of his tongue. "That was never a custom in Germany," he said. "Times were hard between the two wars.
We took care of everything we had." And then he said the
unexpected thing. "We'd have done better if we'd taken care
of our form of government," he said, the poison of failure
pulling at his mouth.

"What did you do about it at the time?" the American
woman asked.

"I? Oh, I didn't join their party, I can assure you of that," he
said. "My father was a monarchist. I myself am one, and
a monarchist I'll die." He said he had been a judge in a Fulda
district court until 1936, and then the powers had eased him
out. First, his position went, and then his pension, and then
the capital he'd put away. "And whether the German people
ever wanted what they got, or got what they wanted, or
wanted it for any length of time after they had it, I could not
have told you then and I cannot tell you now. As a judge, I
had no way of knowing what was taking place in the minds
or the lives of the common people," he said, and he tossed
with impatience at the thought of them.

"But, as a judge, the common people were there in court
before you," the woman said. "You must have heard their
problems every day."

"A professional man is in no position to know what they are

thinking among themselves," said the judge sharply, in rebuke. "The standards are different, the terminology is not the same. If Hitler had been a university graduate," he said, with the taste of the words virulent on his tongue, "there could never have been a Nazi movement. There would have been no means of communication between him and the folk." The obligations of tradition demanded recognition, respect, he went on. This was why it was incomprehensible to a German that Franklin D. Roosevelt's sons had all become salesmen. "Going from door to door with their wares, I believe," he said, "although I have been given to understand that the father had a university education, in spite of the fact that he had Jewish blood."

Fife's House

Now SUMMER was over, and the children would not be coming into the house any more; school had begun again. But in whatever community classrooms of the Zone the American children sat now, the sound of their voices lingered in this house, which had been built for people of another nationality. All summer, the children had come in from the other back yards, come down the hedge-lined pathway, where garbage cans marked "U.S. Property" stood at each gate, and in through the door that opened into the living room, where some petty official of the I. G. Farben works had sat in righteousness with his family once. Or if this door was closed, the children had climbed in across the window sills, some in child-size M.P. outfits bought at the Post Exchange, with handcuffs jangling at their belts, and others with strings or ribbons tied across their brows and a feather or two stuck upright at the back, warbling their Indian war cries as they came. They would mount the stairs looking for Fife, who was six that summer, sometimes half a dozen of them at a time and sometimes more—little girls in sun suits bought at Macy's or Bloomingdale's (or the Midwestern or Southern equivalent of these), or else picked from a Sears, Roebuck catalogue page, and little boys in faded corduroys and striped T shirts, coming barefoot or with soiled canvas sneakers on their feet, invading every corner of the Army-requisitioned house in their incurable sociability.

None of them had any last names, these children who crowded into the small, square rooms all summer. They were merely Linda, and Peggy, and Rosemary, and Joan, or else Douglas, and Michael, and Edwin, and Bill. And there were those who did not stay long enough in the block to be identified by any name—strangers in blue jeans or seersucker who came once or twice, in curiosity, to see Fife's crane work or to listen to his phonograph records before they moved away. But whoever they were or however long they stayed, they would come into the room where Fife's mother sat typing on her bed, and they would talk of the Stateside places that had been their homes once, and of the bikes and roller skates and the Flexible Flyers that had been theirs before they had had to come and live in Germany.

"Bluebells, cockleshells, evie, ivy, over," the children's voices would begin in the morning on the path, which ran the length of the block in back. These were the skipping-rope jumpers, and "Your mother, my mother, live across the way!"

they would sing, skipping out the rhythm of it as they came. They and the M.P.s and the Indians would pass through the I. G. Farben official's living room and mount the stairs to where Fife's mother sat, and they would lean their tanned arms and place their skipping ropes and their handcuffs on the papers scattered on the table by the bed, and her fingers would come to a halt on the typewriter keys. "Why is half of the ribbon black and the other half red?" Rosemary, or Linda, or Joan, might ask, and Fife would know the answer.

"The red is to write the exciting things with," he would say, "and the black is to write the ordinary things, like—you know, 'Once upon a time' or 'So the next day.' "

"Go to the end of the line, so we can hear the bell ring," the M.P.s or the Indians might plead, or they might ask for the carbon paper that was too worn to use any more.

The back yard of Fife's house was the same as every other back yard in the double block of identical two-story, attached houses, except that the lilac bushes by the cement steps, and the sour-cherry tree in the middle of it, had grown taller than those in the other yards. It was perhaps that the official who had lived there once had been allocated a greater share of sunshine than the others, because of particular services he had rendered the chemical industry. But, however it was, only the sour-cherry tree in Fife's yard was strong enough to hold a rope swing on one of its branches, and right after breakfast the children would come to it, as noisy as starlings in the spring. They would fight for a turn on its plank seat and twist its rope into a spiral as they sat on it, for the pleasure of unwinding again in furious rapidity. These were the rope-swing swingers, and there were other groups that came. There were the doll-coach pushers, and the tricyclists, and those who drove their soapbox cars as far as the steps and parked them there before entering the house, calling out Fife's name as they came.

"Can Fife come out?" the voices would ask, and, loud and shrill in half a dozen voices, the "ack-ack-ack-ack" of anti-aircraft fire would begin as Fife slid down the banisters, or down the rain pipe to the yard below.

Fife was small and slender and quick, and the back of his neck was burned dark by the sun. His eyes were blue, and in spite of the visions of Superman and Captain Marvel Jr. and the Man with the Automatic Brain that dwelled within them, they were as gentle and long-lashed as a poet's eyes. There were a few things that Fife owned with pride: a toy garage filled with partially or totally disabled trucks, trailers, and cars, and a Flit spray gun and an egg beater, both of which functioned imperfectly. But in a different class from these was a wristwatch his father had bought him in Switzerland, which was kept in a silk-lined box in his mother's bureau drawer. It had a delicate, copper-colored face, and a stop-watch gadget on its bevelled rim, and, besides hours and minutes and seconds, the days of the month unfolded on it, and the muta-tions of the moon were marked on its disc, in accordance with the rising and waxing and waning and setting of the true moon in the sky. On the occasions when Fife had worn it for a little while—on Sundays, and on his birthday once—it had hung cumbersome as a clock on his wrist, for it was made for a man, and only when he became twelve would it be his to keep and wear.

Fife could wail like a fire engine for unbroken periods of time, and he could imitate with distressing accuracy the whir-ring of the motor of a car that will not start. He could repro-duce the whine of a dive-bomber as it dived, and the sound of airplane wings ripping, in full flight, from a fuselage. And he would reproduce these sounds, and others like them, over and over, as if they were music in his ears. So when the fish game was inaugurated, sometime in August, it brought a curious quiet to the yard and house. It began when Rosemary's father was transferred to Heidelberg, and Rosemary gave her goldfish to Fife before she moved away. This respite came in the hottest part of summer, and Fife and the other children drifted in nearly perfect silence through the living room and up the stairs toward the steady ticking of the mother's typing, their tanned arms in their T shirts weaving through the currents of this mutual vision while their mouths opened and closed, opened and closed, emitting no sound.

How many hours, or days, or weeks, the children might have continued to swim cannot be said, for hardly had this begun when, one afternoon, Fife found the German boy called Horst, and then everything was altered, and nobody came into the garden, and no one played the fish game any more.

It happened because the pathway that ran the length of the block behind the houses stopped short at the broken asphalt of a pavement, in a little clearing of parched, worn grass. And twice in the week the housemen rolled the garbage cans down the path to this clearing for collection, and twice in the week German children came in from the outer avenues and lifted the lids marked "U.S. Property," and went through the refuse that lay inside. Whenever this took place, Fife and the others gathered to watch the German children in envy as they sorted and selected, and carried away the things they wanted. And one afternoon a tall, strong boy in leather shorts was there for the first time among the others, salvaging the best from the stack of garbage cans. His name was Horst, and he was ten,

Fife told his mother, having brought him in pride and awe, with a rucksack hanging on his shoulders, into her room, where she sat on the bed with the typewriter on her knees.

"He's got real deerhorn buttons on his pants," Fife said. There he stood before her, small, almost puny, beside the German boy, with his thin chest rising and falling fast. Horst's hair was flaxen, and it grew gracefully on his head. His cheeks were downy as peach skin in the summer light, and his long, bare arms and thighs were muscular and brown. "He says he'll be my friend," Fife said, and with these words the lineaments of the others—their blue jeans, their sun suits, and their familiar faces—were erased as drawings on a blackboard are erased. The voices of the skipping-rope jumpers droning "Evie, ivy, over" and the war cries of the Indians were heard only faintly and far away, through the window that stood open on the yard below. "His father shot the deer himself, and Horst helped him cut the horns off," Fife said, and the German boy's light eyes were fixed without emotion on him. "His father's a hunter," Fife said.

"What your father do?" Horst asked, saying it in a stubborn, untroubled English to him, and the mother, with her typewriter, might not have been in the room with them, for he did not look her way.

"Oh, he works in Military Government," Fife said, but this was of no importance and he went on quickly, "I'd like to go hunting," and he looked in shy, bleak hope now at the other boy.

"You get bullets, my father take you hunting," Horst said. He ran his thumbs inside the rucksack straps and jerked the full bag higher on his back. "My father need bullets. You get him bullets," he said, and Fife stood nodding his head in acquiescence before this figure of strength and comeliness that had taken shape before his eyes.

"Maybe Fife's a little too young to go hunting yet," Fife's mother said, but the words sounded frail and feminine in her own ears as she said them, the protest irrational and impotent.

Horst turned his head on his strong, sunburned neck, and he looked for the first time, and without any sign of interest, at her. "First time I go hunting, I'm four," he said.

This was the way it began, and in the days that followed the swingers no longer gathered at the swing behind the house, and the doll-coach pushers moved, two by two or in single file, in other directions. The Indian war cries sounded in the distance now, and the skipping-rope jumpers' voices said faintly, as if in sorrow, "Daisy, Daisy, touch the ground. Daisy, Daisy, turn around," but they did not come near. Fife's room was at the end of the hall, and Fife and Horst stayed there together, not playing on the floor with cars that wound up with a key, and not listening to the phonograph records, but talking in lowered voices, with circumspect pauses between their sentences, as older people talk. And on the second or third morning Fife came down the hall to his mother's room, coming quietly through the half-open door, and halted beside the bed.

"Look," he said, and he drew one finger along the painted metal of her typewriter. "That wristwatch you're keeping for me—it's my wristwatch, isn't it?"

"It's going to be yours," said his mother, and she went on typing, so that she need not see the tight white mark of pain around his mouth.

"Well, if it's mine, I can do what I want with it, can't I?" Fife said, but he still did not look into her face. "I told Horst about my wristwatch, and that's the kind of wristwatch he wants. If I give it to him, his father's going to take me hunting," he said.

"But you can't give something away that isn't yours yet," his mother said, and her fingers halted now on the typewriter keys. "You can't just skip five or six years like that. It's like trying to make Christmas come in the middle of summer."

"You told me Christmas comes in the middle of summer in Australia," Fife said.

That wasn't the end of it; it was nowhere near the end of it. In the afternoon, it was Horst himself who stood, bronzed and tall and handsome on the threshold of the room, looking Fife's mother in the eye. This time he wore black leather shorts, with edelweiss embroidered on the suède-like braces of them, and his blond hair gleamed as clear as light on the edge of the dim, shuttered room.

"I come for the vatch," Horst said. Behind him, small as one of the gnomes on his bibbed blue jeans, Fife lingered in the shadows of the hall.

"It doesn't belong to Fife yet," said the mother, and she slowly "X"ed out the last words she had written, for they were not the words she had wanted to set down. "He has to wait until he's older, and then he can do what he wants with it."

"O.K. I vait *bis* five o'clock," Horst said.

During this week in the summer when the children came no longer to the house, there was no language to speak to Fife in, for the substance of his being had seemed to change. He had entered an errant male world from which neither mother nor fellow countrymen could recall him, and in the early morning there was the sound of only one boy's footsteps coming up the stairs. Day after day, the two boys' voices murmured in Fife's room at the end of the hall, but it was only when the mother paused in her typing that she could hear the words they said. The argument may always have been the same one, for the bits and pieces of it were concerned with interchange and barter, and the mother heard Fife offer his Flit gun to Horst, and heard the gasp and wheeze of it as the German boy tried it, before the air pump jammed.

"It only jams every other time, not every time," Fife said in a low voice.

"I take the vatch instead," Horst said, and she heard him put the sprayer down.

Horst did not want the toy garage, or the cars that were in it, but it may have been that he considered for a moment the egg beater, which Fife kept under his pillow when he went to sleep, for the mother could hear the whirring of its flections. And then the sound of rotating ceased abruptly and there was silence in Fife's room and in the hall.

"When it sticks like that, all you have to do is turn the handle a little bit the other way. Like this," Fife said, and he seemed to be working with it. "It's a pretty good egg beater except for that one thing," he said.

"I don't vant it," said Horst, and the mother did not hear what he went on saying, for she had begun her typewriting again.

And then, at the end of the week, they made a final bid for the watch. They came to the mother's room, one bronze-limbed and flaxen-haired and tall, and the other almost dwarfed beside him in his shabby overalls.

"I wanted to show him my wristwatch," Fife said. "Just to show it to him."

"All right," said his mother, and she kept her eyes on the last line she had written. "Look at it quickly and then go away."

She did not have to turn her head to know how Fife would lift it from the silk-lined box. She could feel the delicacy and caution in his fingers as palpably as if he touched, not a cold gold shell in which the instants of life ticked brightly, mechanically, away, but the swift, impatient pulsing of her heart. She did not look up from the page before her until they had started toward the door.

"I vear it home tonight. I show my father," Horst said, and she saw that he had strapped it on his own brown wrist. "I bring it back O.K. tomorrow," he said.

"Look, Horst," said the mother, and now she set the typewriter aside, and she swung her legs in the blue silk housecoat down from the I. G. Farben official's varnished bed.

"He'll bring it back tomorrow. He just said he would," Fife said, but his dusty sandals wavered in pain and indecision on the shade-and-sun striped floor.

"Horst, I'm sorry. His father wouldn't like it," Fife's mother said.

"My father—" Horst began, but he did not go on with it. Instead, a look of fury came into his cold, light eyes. "That vatch not gold. I don't take it. I don't vant something phony," he said. He jerked the strap of it free of the buckle, and he tossed the wristwatch from him, toward where the mother sat upon the bed. It struck hard against the metal of the typewriter and fell upon the flowered cover with its coppery-colored gold face down. Once this was done, nobody moved, nobody seemed to draw breath in the room, and then Fife whirled on his dusty sandals, and he drove his fierce, small,

96

unaccustomed fists into Horst's impervious flesh and bone.

That was the last time they saw Horst. He may have come back sometime in the evening of that same day, but that they never knew. It was known only that after dusk spirals of smoke began to rise in the hot, still air, each helix of it rising from each gate cut in the double hedgerow, and, standing at the open window, Fife's mother saw that the lids had been lifted and that flames were fanning, indolent and loose and golden, in the open garbage cans. There had been no outcry, no sound of footsteps rushing down the pathway, and yet these fires of rubbish burning had served as signals for assemblage. For now the children came out of their houses into the summer evening, came with watering cans and saucepans filled and splashing over as they ran across the grass. The skipping-rope jumpers and the rope-swing swingers and the soapbox drivers and the Indians crowded in ecstasy and disorder onto the common pathway, and, shouting and screaming, they fled from garbage can to garbage can, flinging the water they carried in upon the flames. The child-size M.P.s had fixed a garden hose to the faucet of one kitchen sink, and they played the jet that sprang from it onto the fires, while the others ran back through the yards, their voices piercing the evening air, to fill their receptacles again.

No bell had sounded out in summons, but after a moment Fife opened the door of his own silent room, and he came down the hall and crossed the threshold to where his mother stood.

"I can smell smoke, can't you?" he said, and he and his mother did not look into each other's faces yet but out across the lilac trees.

"Someone set fire to the garbage cans," his mother said, and

Fife swung himself by his thin, braced arms onto the window sill.

"Golly, the whole row's burning!" he said, kneeling in wonder on the broad stone ledge.

Now the doll-coach pushers came hastening out, one behind another, the doll coaches careening crazily before them as they ran. The cushions, the covers, the dolls themselves—all the paraphernalia of motherhood—were gone, and the coaches carried tins of water. And with each slap of it cast on the flames it seemed to the mother that the hot, sore memory of Horst, and the features of his face, and the words he had said were extinguished. He was nowhere among the wildly leaping others as Fife stood up, holding with his hands to the iron ribs of the lifted blind, and moved on his rubber-soled sandals to the edge, and slid, calling their names out hoarsely as he went, down the rain pipe to the yard below.

Summer Evening

Toward seven o'clock of a dreamy, bluish summer evening, the cocktail party, which was taking place at a terraced villa overlooking the eleventh-century Hessian town across the valley, was well under way. The first guests had come scarcely an hour before, driving up the hill in their shining American cars, and now, some in uniform, others in civilian clothes, they strolled out through the long open windows onto the gravel of the upper terrace, bearing their frosted glasses with them and talking and laughing as they came. On the opposite hill, the ancient *Schloss* rose, sombre and monumental, above the treetops, its façade and turrets turned toward the widening river valley, appearing to watch, as it had watched century after century, for armored knights on horseback to take shape

99

in the twilight of the distance, or for armored vehicles and low-flying planes to advance, as they had come in April, four years before, out of the area of perpetual dusk that lay fifteen or twenty miles away.

Except for the German musicians, who bent their heads to violin and zither and accordion, and for the *Hausmeister*, in his starched white jacket, who moved among the guests, there were only Americans present, and it was their voices, both men's and women's, and their laughter that rang out above the tender striving of the instruments as the music cast its spell of longing on the summery air. For the uniformed men who leaned on the balustrade or who strolled on the terrace were officers of the American Army of Occupation, and the civilians were men attached to the Military Government offices—men, some with wives and some without, whom the call of duty had brought to this defeated land. But to anyone passing on the road below the garden wall it might have seemed that it was the Americans who were at ease on a familiar soil and the musicians, playing their nostalgic music, who were exiled from a homeland that lay far across the sea.

"You have to be as careful about who you take for a *Hausmeister* as who you marry," Major Hatches was saying to the view of the peaceful valley and the town and the domineering *Schloss* above it. He was a handsome figure of an officer, probably forty-five but appearing younger, standing, spruce and lean in his green blouse and his pinks, against the deepening tide of twilight, with his glass held in his boyish hand. "You have him underfoot twenty-four hours every day of the week," he was saying to the pretty women—Occupation wives with brightly painted mouths and glossy hair—and to the younger officers in the group around him by the balustrade.

"He knows how many cigarette stubs you can be counted on leaving in which ashtrays between the morning shower and the time you leave the house," the Major said, and he took a chopped-egg-and-anchovy canapé from the platter before it passed from reach.

"Fellow I knew down in Nuremberg used to fox his *Hausmeister* every time," said Lieutenant Pearson, already beginning, or perhaps never, even in sleep, having quite ceased, to laugh. He stood six feet tall, and despite his youth three rolls of flesh lay on his jacket collar, for his good nature had larded him since childhood with excessive fat. "Used to drop his stubs out of the window, so the guy'd have to crawl through the shrubbery for them," he said, shaking with laughter, and he drew one plump hand across the bristles of his close-cropped hair.

"That's not according to Hoyle," said the Major, whatever there was of reprimand in it tempered by his smile. "It's one of the articles of the Occupation Statute that you leave your cigarette stubs in plain sight," he said, and the group around joined in Lieutenant Pearson's laughter. He stood there shaking, with his cheeks squeezed up as if in actual pain. "A *Hausmeister* 'll make enough out of what's left in the ashtrays after one of these shindigs to keep him in luxury six months," the Major went on. He jerked his chin after the stooped man in the clean white jacket who bore the platter of canapés from guest to animated guest—an aging man, with his legs warped in his shrunk cotton trousers, and his thin gray hair combed neatly on his skull. "Ours has to be watched. He has a weakness for the bottle," he said, and he drank from the depths of the ice-and-fruit-encumbered glass he held.

Beyond them, in the thick of the fray, Mrs. Hatches flew at

her guests with cries of pleasure, her bosom swollen like a pigeon's in her flowered dress. She was older than the Major, and she bore the knowledge of this with some hysteria, painting her soft-jowled face high in denial of it and tinting her iron-gray hair blue.

"That's twice you-all gave you' wud you'd come on ovah and play bridge with the Majah and me!" she might cry aloud as she fled among them, but it was not their faces that had meaning for her. While the Major was a lieutenant still, her blank, dazzled eyes had been blinded to recognition of any man's or woman's features, placing them only by company and field grade, so civilians always troubled her. "You promised me that lemon-meringue recipe two weeks ago," she might cry out in her uncertainty, "an' you nevah kep' you' wud!"

But because of the longing of the music and the gentleness of the evening the attention of the guests was not held by these subjects but wandered to far sweeter and stranger things. The men's thoughts were concerned with the charm of the women in their fresh light dresses, and their unexpected beauty in the fading light, and the women, drinking quickly, viewed with excitement the homage offered in the men's attentive faces, knowing that in this interval all dreams and all desire were contained in the rising and falling of their laughter, and in the stirring of their limbs within their clothes. There was, for instance, Marcia Cruickshank, lying back in the wicker chair, drinking her drink, and looking in lazy shamelessness at the young man seated on the terrace balustrade.

"You're new," she said, liking the bronze of sunburn on his hands and neck and brow.

"Berlin," he said. He was wearing a well-cut navy-blue suit and a conservative tie, with the white of his silk shirt pleasing to see against the clear brown of his skin. He had lit a cigarette now, and he sat looking down at Marcia Cruickshank, whose eyes were wide-set in her blond, Nordic face, eyes aquamarine in color and transparent. Beneath them, her high cheekbones were flushed with the fever of either drink or love.

"I've been here a year. I'm going crazy," she said, her voice husky and low. Her arms were naked to the shoulder and as white as milk, and her hair was brushed up, light and silky, on her head. Her legs were stretched from under the gray stuff of her dress, long and smooth-skinned, and the young man followed the line of them with his cool, dark, diabolical eyes. "So tan, aren't you? So really athletic?" said Marcia Cruickshank, her voice too languorous for mockery.

"Tennis," the young man said, not looking at her face.

"Oh, God! When you're not married, there's time for everything," she said, saying it softly, lazily, still, but speaking bitterly.

"Not quite for everything," the young man said. He might have been asking her now for what he wanted of her, except for the casualness of his hand as he tapped the ashes from his cigarette. "I'm with Intelligence," he said quietly. "That means eighteen hours a day. I've never had time, for example, to play house with anyone like you."

But the *Hausmeister* had come between them now, and the young man took a canapé from his platter, and Marcia Cruickshank stirred in the deep-seated wicker chair and offered the *Hausmeister* a Camel from her pack. He had a queer sort of twist to his body, which gave him a dwarfed, gnomelike look, it being doubtless lumbago that had closed on the small of his back a long time since and caused his spine to slip a vertebra or two. His false teeth were bared in his leathery face, in a grimace intended to express his deference, and he quivered with pleasure when Marcia Cruickshank reached out her hand, with the fingernails varnished scarlet on it, and laid it on his arm.

"For God's sake, go and have yourself an Old-Fashioned, Pop," she said. "Just get behind the pantry door and have a quick one. It's the only way to beat the rap," she said.

"Old Pop's O.K.," said the *Hausmeister*, but a bead of self-commiseration stood bright in the corner of each eye. "Good German music. Makes Pop remember other times," he said. He shifted the platter of canapés from one hand to the other to take the cigarette from her pack. "Everything bombed out. Everything lost. Nothing left to Pop," he said. When he had put the cigarette into his jacket pocket, he pulled himself nearly erect, brought his heels together, and saluted Marcia Cruickshank with his stiffly cupped right hand brought smartly from temple to brow.

"Now give it a rest, dear," said Marcia Cruickshank wearily, and the young man sitting on the balustrade turned his head to watch the *Hausmeister* sidle humbly, grievously, away.

"Pretty tough on some of these old boys," the young man said, and Marcia Cruickshank looked lazily up at him, at the line of his throat and jaw, and the cool, dark, diabolical eyes.

"Probably had great, big, luxurious concentration camps of their own once," she said, putting a catch of emotion in her voice. "And now what have they got? Nothing but Scotch and rye."

"Your glass is empty, Mrs. Cruickshank. It is *Mrs.* Cruickshank, isn't it?" he said.

"I wish to God it wasn't," said Marcia Cruickshank, in sudden bitterness. "I like to look at you. I like to listen to you."

"I'm going to get us another drink. We can talk better after another drink," he said, and he slid down from the balustrade.

"Don't go," whispered Marcia Cruickshank, scarcely aloud. "For God's sake, don't go."

Captain Pete Forsythe stood a little apart from the central groups of animation, his back leaning in comfort against the grapevine whose pallid, flexile leaves spread across this side of the house. He was nursing a glass of Scotch-and-soda in one hand, his mouth smiling gently, his half-closed eyes reflecting on the beauty of the valley, as the young man in the dark-blue suit came past in search of drink.

"I'm against it. I'm against organized, uniformed annihilation," Captain Forsythe said, in a quiet voice. He was slight, sandy-haired, and barely thirty, and he had stopped the young man who was passing merely by looking straight into his eyes.

"That depends on who gets annihilated," said the young man, making it light, but his glance was tense as it moved across the people, seeking the *Hausmeister* out.

"Over there," said Captain Forsythe, his voice gentle as he looked across the valley to where the *Schloss* stood, drawn in sharp relief now against the yellowish sky, "over there— the other side of the hill—there's a tank, a big Sherman tank, rusted and gutted and turned on its back, with field flowers growing through the carcass of it. I saw it when I rode through the country one day last week. It made me think of the wreckage of fighter planes that we used to see in the fields near Carthage—engines and fuselage more archaic than the two-thousand-year-old stone plows the oxen were dragging through the soil perhaps five yards away. The meaningless paraphernalia of war," said Captain Forsythe, as if speaking from a dream, and the young man's cool, dark eyes surveyed him carefully, with a certain shrewdness even, as the Captain lifted his glass to drink. Had it not been for Mrs. Hatches, he might have encouraged the Captain to go on with it, but Mrs. Hatches had run toward them, crying aloud, the gravel and her heels conniving to produce her wild, unbalanced gait.

"Why, that's agains' all the rewls!" she cried out. "The tew of you standin' up theyah talkin' togetheh, sobah as jedges, and one without a glass to cheah him! Now, we cain't have anythin' like that!" she cried, and her eye, too, was sharp for where the *Hausmeister* might be. Because she was drawn to no man's flesh in lust or love, and no man's flesh was drawn to hers, nothing remained to her but to flee like one possessed among the drinking, laughing people, as if in flight before the lonely spectre of old age. She would seize up empty glasses to fill them anew, crying the *Hausmeister's* name aloud in panic when she could not find the stooped white shoulders of his jacket sidling through the dusk; calling him to bear more sausages stabbed with toothpicks out, more brimming glasses, and to pass them with greater speed among the guests, urging him to race, neck and neck, with her on the homestretch of social vigilance before the field grades would begin to go. If ever she let him from her sight, she knew he would sidle to the whining of the music, to the rear, and get one or two drinks down behind the kitchen door. "Now let's the three of us—Pete Fo'sythe and you and me—" Mrs. Hatches began, but was interrupted by the personable young man whose civilian rating she did not know.

"Please allow me to go for the drinks," the young man said, and he escaped them, making note of the name Forsythe and thinking in controlled hot passion of Marcia Cruickshank's milk-white legs and her naked arms as he stepped in absolute composure through the long window, which stood open like a door.

Captain Pete Forsythe, still leaning against the vine leaves, lifted his glass and drank before he spoke. "You're standing on my wife," he said in his quiet voice, and Mrs. Hatches looked behind her hastily and gave a loud, apologetic cry. There, on a garden footstool, obscured by the vines and by the gathering darkness, sat a slender, fawn-eyed girl in a low-cut scarlet dress, with the lengths of it spread around her on the pebbled ground. "My wife has been crying," said Captain Forsythe, with the contemplative smile on his tilted mouth. "We read Proust until late last night, and the world was re-created. Then you come awake."

"Oh, Pete, Pete, my love," said Mrs. Forsythe from where she sat, below them, "I'm not crying for a dream. The dreams are finished. They've all curdled in my heart," she said. She was perhaps twenty, with a teenlike thinness in her bones still, and her face was as delicate as a flower, with the fawn eyes and the soft mouth too big, too vulnerable, in it, and filled now with a passionate gravity. Behind each ear was thrust a fragrant live rose of the same rich color as her dress, and these held back her feathery dark hair. "I'm weak as water. I hate it, but I'm weak," she said, and she looked up in supplication at the faces that were there above. "I'm crying for a reality, Mrs. Hatches, not for a dream that Proust lived once. I'm crying for the whooping cranes, who stand as tall as the Indians who hunted them, and who are going to die."

"Wendy, I don't think you' feelin' quite yo'self," the Major's wife said. "Let's you and I go inside the house togetheh and have a cup of coffee, jus' us tew," she said, but Mrs. Forsythe might not have heard her speak.

"I don't want a world like this," she said. "I don't want a world in which birds who stand as tall as men are wiped away."

"Pete Fo'sythe, you git along and git yo'self anotheh drink while I have a little talk with Wendy," Mrs. Hatches said, but Captain Forsythe did not go. He set his empty glass down on the window sill beside him, instead, and he folded his arms across the breast of his battle jacket, and his head moved to the pain and beauty of the music that the violin and zither and accordion played.

"Like the Labrador duck, the passenger pigeon, and the heath hen," he said, saying it slowly, like the words of a line of poetry he was trying to recall, "like the great auk, and the ivory-billed woodpecker, like man himself, the whooping crane is doomed to go." He leaned back at his ease against the wall, his half-closed eyes looking past the talking, drinking people on the terrace, which was partially lit now from the lamps that had been lighted, one by one, within the house as the twilight died. The outline of the hills that enclosed the valley was gone, and the *Schloss* was lost in darkness, and the musicians' instruments cried sweetly, piercingly, in the night for the look of one city, for the streets and the parks, for the stones and the trees, the wine cellars, the palaces, the wit, and the women of Vienna, as the stars came, far and isolate, into the Hessian sky. But Captain Forsythe's thoughts had nothing to do with these things, this place; it was the vast expanse of another country that he saw stretching away. "The wheat growers came down across the plains and the marshes and the open prairies," he was saying softly, "and the whooping crane lost its breeding ground. Like the Indian, the bison, the poets,

108

their time is finished. There is no role left for them to play."

"So they are asked to take their wingspread somewhere else," said Mrs. Forsythe. She sat on the footstool below them still, pressing her two hands tight between her knees. "It's pure white and greater than an archangel's, but there is no place but extinction left for it to go. I read about one, Mrs. Hatches, who had lost an eye and broken a wing, and they put him in a refuge," she said, speaking quickly. "They offered him the Mackenzie Delta, and Iowa, and a part of western Illinois, and the region stretching from southwestern Louisiana to Mexico. Because that's what they'll do for you when you can't fly any more and are nearly extinct," she said, her voice almost breaking with its grief. "But it wasn't that that he wanted, Mrs. Hatches. He wanted a mate, he wanted a wife, so the kind of thing they had been for centuries wouldn't have to be extinct," and her tears began to fall.

"He wanted a thin, sweet wife," said Captain Forsythe softly, "with red roses stuck behind her ears."

A feeling of space, of peace, seemed to spread across the terrace now; it might have been that a burden had been lifted, that they were given air to breathe, for the guests were thinning out at last. Mrs. Hatches' glance fled here and there in inquiry, noted that Colonel and Mrs. Smith and the senior Military Government officer and his wife no longer stood chatting by the balustrade, and that the Major stood on the stone steps that led down to the drive, which curved below the lower terrace, calling goodbye to the headlights of the departing cars. The *Hausmeister*, thought Mrs. Hatches, in sudden panic, and she began to run from uniform to uniform, insignia to insignia again, among the scattered people who remained.

The *Hausmeister*, she thought, with determination, her eyes outraged by the overturned glasses, the cluttered ashtrays, the canapé platters littered with olive stones and soiled by mayonnaise. The music came abruptly to an end, for Lieutenant Pearson had taken the violin from the musician's hands and now sought to accompany on the delicate catgut strings his own loud, jovial rendering of "Clementine."

"How'm I doin'?" he called out to Mrs. Hatches as she passed, his flesh convulsed with laughter.

"Why, fine, jes' fine!" said Mrs. Hatches, crossing the gravel on her high, unsteady heels. As she reached the long open window that served as door, Captain Cruickshank came through it, his young eyes bloodshot, holding his wife upright against him, urging her limp legs to bear her on at least as far as the driveway and the car. Marcia Cruickshank's mouth was clean of lipstick, her eyes were sightless, and her face was bleached colorless from drink.

"It happens every damned time. Every damned time we go out, it happens," said Captain Cruickshank, swaying forward. In the brief moment that they faltered there, Captain Cruickshank's face was not that of an officer any longer but of a tired, disappointed boy, perhaps having learned just then, at that instant, that the ball game had been called off forever, the swimming hole been permanently drained dry. "She ought to stick to lemonade," said Captain Cruickshank, and Mrs. Hatches smiled politely and hurried past them, her voice quite musical as she called out the *Hausmeister's* name.

But even after the other guests and the musicians were gone, Lieutenant Pearson and the young man in the dark-blue suit lingered by the balustrade. The Major had offered them a final drink, and as they talked together on the half-lit terrace the young man rubbed discreetly with his Scotch-plaid handkerchief in quiet colors at the stain of lip salve that lingered on his mouth. The Major was speaking in satisfaction of antiques to them, his tongue only slightly thick as he said the collecting of antique silver and handmade linens and porcelain was one of the artistic pursuits that he and Mrs. Hatches shared.

"We picked up some very fine pieces over here while times were hard still," the Major said, standing tall and elegant and almost steady against the stars. "Museum pieces, in their way. I'd like to show them to you sometime. We've got a Biedermeier silver coffee set that had been handed down from one generation to the next, without a scratch on it. And my wife got hold of a seventy-four-piece Dresden dinner service with gold inlay. I know they're going to mean a lot to us when we get home," he said.

"I see you're a connoisseur," said the young man in the navy-blue suit, and he folded his handkerchief carefully and put it away. "Let me tell you that Berlin's the territory for the man who's got a flair. They're still pretty hungry over there, so they come to terms without too much of an argument." His tanned face was illuminated for an instant as he took a light from the match Lieutenant Pearson held. "I picked up a tablecloth from a professor's wife last week who'd spent twenty years making it. Every inch of it lace. You'd appreciate it, Major. Experts tell me it's a thing that would bring five to six hundred dollars at home." The Major gave a long, slow whistle as he poured them each another drink. "I got it for a song," the young man said.

"Which one?" asked Lieutenant Pearson, his eyes squeezed small by his firm, shining cheeks, his mouth distorted by his silent mirth. " 'Lili Marlene' or 'Dinah, Won't You Blow'?"

"They'll part with their back teeth if you have coffee or lard," the young man said, in answer.

"Just for future reference, in tins or in the bean?" the Major said.

"They don't make conditions over there. The market's good still," said the young man sitting smoking on the balustrade.

It was then that the *Hausmeister* appeared before them, having arisen, it seemed, from the shrubbery of the terrace below. He came, weary and stooped, his starched white jacket shining like moonlight in the dark, his warped legs rocking under him, emerging from the deep, cool well of night and coming up the stone steps from the drive.

"Pop, I bet you've been snaring cigarette stubs again!" said Lieutenant Pearson, beginning to laugh.

"Pop, come and have a drink," Major Hatches said, in kindness, at the sight of him standing there, leather-skinned, gnome-wizened, small.

"Major, I want speak to you," the *Hausmeister* said, his bright, grieving eyes, which belied the deferential eternal grimace of the china teeth, turned sharp now as he watched the Major pour the whiskey unsteadily out. "I'm American man. I want go home to U.S.A."

"American?" said the Major. He handed the glass to the *Hausmeister*, and then he turned to the balustrade and set the bottle down.

"Sure, and I'm Rooshun" said Lieutenant Pearson, and he rubbed his big, dimpled hands together in delight. "Paderewski, *nyet, stoi*, Henry Wallace!"

112

"My mother, she American woman," said the *Hausmeister*, the glass of whiskey swinging in his aged, gnarled hand. "She *geboren* New Joisey. She no Joiman. She married wid a Joiman."

"Now, let's get this straight," said the Major. He could hear his wife calling the *Hausmeister's* name as she stood in the long open window for a moment, and then she must have perceived him standing there drinking with the others, for she turned back in to the lighted living room again. "You say your mother was born in New Jersey, Pop," the Major said, but he felt too weary, too confused, to bother with any of it any more.

"I *geboren* in New Joisey by my mother," the *Hausmeister* said, with a certain ferocity. "Den my father, he take us to Joimany." After he had said this, he looked in sudden, bleak appeal at the three men there before him. "I want American passport. I go home to U.S.A.," he said.

"Sure," said Lieutenant Pearson, and he gave the Major a wink. "Sure you do, Pop," he said. He lifted one soft, heavy arm in his battle jacket, and laid it around the shoulders of the young man in the dark-blue suit, by this gesture abruptly dwarfing him, making a frail and irresolute figure of him merely by the proximity of his own outlandish weight and size. "Here's who you want to talk to," said Lieutenant Pearson. "Here's the American Consul General, just in from Berlin. Here's the only man in the E.C. who can get a passport for you overnight," he said, for once not laughing, for once the hard-packed rolls and creases of his swollen face immobilized by gravity.

"No kiddin'?" the *Hausmeister* said. For an instant, the warped legs ceased to rock.

"Cross my heart, hope to die," said Lieutenant Pearson, saying it as a boy might have, not as a drunk man seeking to maintain with dignity a fat boy's innocent, unsmiling mien. He looked down at the young man, his arm half crippled, half embraced. "How about it, Consul General?" he said.

They did not know it was going to be like this; they did not expect the *Hausmeister* to cry any more than they expected him to say his age was seventy-three. But once the young man had accepted the role of Consul General, the thing had already gone beyond them; it had become, of its own momentum, something that two other men were acting out on another terrace, with no sense and no humor in it, and no way to bring it to an end. The young man in civilian dress had found a bridge score card in his pocket, and as the *Hausmeister* gave them to him, he set the names, the dates, the two words of a place, "New Joisey," spelling it like that, on the lines of the score card, with the greatest care.

"You get me passport? You get me passport to U.S.A.?" the *Hausmeister* asked, watching the hieroglyphics being written down.

"Sure, he's going to give you a passport. He's going to give you a passport, Pop. Now all you need is an airline ticket," Lieutenant Pearson said. The waves of nausea were rising in him, the taste bad in his mouth. And then the sobs began to rip from the *Hausmeister's* breast, the sound of them akin to foolish laughter, and the tears of helpless gratitude streamed from his eyes. "You just get four photographs taken," Lieutenant Pearson said, and whatever it was that had sustained him until now collapsed within him, and he slid down between the young man and the Major and came to rest on the gravel of the terrace, his head and shoulders at ease against the pillars of the balustrade.

"Stop crying!" the Major roared suddenly, and the *Hausmeister* drew himself nearly erect, put his empty glass in his left hand as he brought his heels together, lifted his chin, raised his right arm in the starched white sleeve, and cupped his hand stiffly at his temple, in salute. "Seventy-three, and crying like a child!" the Major said. He reached out and took the score card from the young man's hand. "We'll have another drink around, and then we'll put Pearson and ourselves to bed," he said, and he tore the score card in two. Then he stood motionless, silent, a moment, not only surveying the men before him but looking in wonder and question upon himself as well. *What are we doing here, any of us?* he asked himself, in sudden bewilderment, almost in fright. *What has become of the lot of us here?* "Go get some soda and ice in the kitchen, Pop," he said.

"Forsythe, Captain Pete Forsythe," said the young man in the dark-blue suit, and it might have been this, or something like it, that he had been saying all the time. He took his cigarette case out of his pocket and offered it to the Major before he selected one himself, watching the *Hausmeister* weave his way over the terrace toward the lighted windows of the house. "Seems a bit on the appeasing side—Captain Forsythe—doesn't he, Major?" he said.

Frankfurt in Our Blood

I<small>T WAS</small> the half bottles of wine which made them speak.
Without them, the two women seated at a small table at the
end of the dining-car might have had nothing to say. Paris lay
barely twenty minutes behind them, but already the gently
sloping green hills and the luxuriant fields of France were
there, streaming swiftly past the windows: the villages, the
feathery trees, the fluid country dimmed now to the quality
of ancient murals by the veil of dusk which lay across the land.
But inside the crowded diner of the Orient Express, the illumination was as hard as brass, and the waiters swayed down
the aisle between the tables, bearing their trays as if upon the
current of a stream.

Behind the diner swung the nimble links of the long racing

train, the sleeping-cars for Prague and Frankfurt coupled with those for Warsaw and Budapest, or with sleepers for Brati-slava, Vienna, Munich, Bucharest. By morning, these cars, which roared through the pastoral stillness of the continent, would have taken their separate ways, shunted off at Bar-le-Duc while the travellers slept within them, and the people who shared tables for the evening meal would have forgotten the look of one another in a little while. The two women were strangers to each other, and the one who rode in the direction in which the train was going was young and soft-skinned, and she wore a blue cotton short-sleeved dress, as simple as a schoolgirl's dress. She sat with her face turned toward the window, and her chin held in the cushion of her ringless left hand. The small stooped aging woman who sat opposite had also turned her head to watch the deepening twilight, her flesh, hair, clothing, eyes, all of the same worn faded gray. But there were the half bottles of red wine before them, and it was the faded little woman who made the first move, and who leaned forward toward the girl.

"Perhaps we could divide a half bottle between us?" she began, her diffidence coming meekly, patiently, to speech. "We could share the expense of it," she said, her accent not quite English and not quite American.

The girl turned back from the window, her wide eyes startled, and she looked at the woman as if waking from a dream.

"Yes, indeed. Yes," she said, and that might have been the end of it. It was the other woman who motioned the waiter to pull the cork of one of the two little bottles of red wine. Once he had done this, and wiped the bottle's dark mouth clean, it was her hand, reaching, narrow and ivory-knuckled, from the suit's gray sleeve, which poured the wine into their glasses with care. The girl had turned to the window again, her hands clasped on the table before her, her soft dark hair hanging long across the shoulders of her dress. "How I hate it," she said, and she looked out at the sight of the fleeing country as she spoke. "How I hate going back to Germany," she said, and she reached quickly and blindly out and took her glass up, and drank down the first swallow of red wine.

"Yes, going back," said the little woman, but she did not drink. Instead, she picked up her gray cotton gloves from where they lay beside her plate, and she laid the wrinkled fingers of them carefully together, and she smoothed them gently, reflectively, out upon her knees. "Yes, going back," she said.

When the woman began to eat the split pea soup, the girl turned away from the window again, and she pushed the metal bowl of her own soup aside. It could be seen that her mouth was bright with lipstick, and blemished by discontent, and that her glossy hair was cut in a fringe above blue baleful eyes. The faded little woman watched her young hand, her bare arm, lift to fill their glasses with the strong good wine.

"Every time it's a little bit harder than it was the time before," the girl was saying quickly. She sat with her arms resting on the table, turning the glass of wine between her fingers on the cloth. "You see, I go to Paris perhaps once a month, just for the week end. And every time I have to go back it's like cutting my heart out and throwing it away."

"And you can't stay in Paris?" the woman said quietly.

"Well, I have a job," the girl said, still watching the glass turn on the cloth. "I'm a War Department civilian in Frankfurt." The waiter had carried the bowls away, the full one

118

inside the empty one, and the girl took another swallow of the wine. "I took the job just to get over. Just to get on the same continent with France," she said, and she lifted one hand to the side of her face as if to shield it, as though there might be tears in her eyes and she did not want a stranger to see them fall.

"Yes, Frankfurt," said the faded little woman. "It's been a long time, but I could tell you the name of almost every street still. You know, I went there as a bride once!" she said, and she lifted her glass of wine again and drank a little, trying to make it sound, even after all the years that had passed, festive and jaunty and gay. "My husband taught in the university there," she said, with a sociable smile on her lips, but her hand as it set the glass down on the cloth again was trembling like a leaf in the high wind of emotion that came sweeping through her heart. She looked at the ham in gravy which the waiter set before her, but she made no move to eat. "We lived there twenty-five years together," she said.

"You have memories. That's a certain kind of wealth," the girl said, seeming to begrudge them to her. "I have absolutely nothing except the things I want to be."

"Well, let's make this into a little celebration," said the woman, and she raised her glass as if they might drink a toast together, but the girl drank quickly, without acknowledging the woman's lifted glass or the tentative smile that hung upon her mouth.

"Six months ago, I didn't believe that Germany would remain for me this alien, evil thing," the girl said, and across the table, the woman looked meekly up at her young face. "I thought I would be able to get close to what it really is, or was," the girl said, speaking quickly, while outside the windows the lights of the villages and the rural stations of France were cast behind them in the dark. "But I see Germany like some isolated territory, like a lepers' colony, an infected island which free men conquered, and who have, because of this, become ailing and evil and no longer free."

"Yes," said the woman, "but, you know, there is a strange thing that can happen to people. Or perhaps when people get older, this is the thing that always happens." The waiter bore the plates away, and the woman sat smiling, smiling almost in apology across the cloth. "I can only think of Germany now as it was when I was a child, and of Frankfurt as I knew it as a bride," she said. And now an unexpected look of audacity, an almost devilish look of mischief came into her worn faded eyes. "You know, I have a little French money left, not much, but enough," she said; "and I would like to spend it on another half bottle of wine!"

The waiter uncorked the second half bottle, and wiped its mouth clean, and then he put the plates of lamb and peas before them. And now that the woman's voice had ceased to speak, the girl turned to the window again, and to the sight of the deepening darkness through which the country flowed swiftly, irretrievably past. Tomorrow there would be Frankfurt, and the bomb-gutted station in the early morning, and the houses laid open to the elements still bearing within their rubble outlandish bits and pieces of what had once been comfort and security. There would be the radiator hanging by its pipes through a floor that had capsized beneath it five years before, and the bathtub standing two stories high above the dead magnolia trees, its clawed feet resting on nothing, and the panelled door behind it still standing ajar.

"Or perhaps the place you began life in as a bride is a place that can never change for you," the woman was saying now, and the girl turned abruptly away from the window, and she poured their glasses full with wine. "There was my husband's work in the university, and there were other professors, and there were artists, too, writers, countless friends," said the little woman, smiling as she spoke. "There we had meetings, discussions, and not only among intellectuals, but among men of the free crafts, the guilds, the unions. For Frankfurt was once the heart of liberal Germany. And then, in 1934, my husband died. He was very wise to choose that year to die in," she said, still smiling, but her hand was shaking as if with palsy as she took the glass of wine. "We are a Jewish family," she said, "so in one way or another we had to go."

"And you, where did you go?" the girl asked, and the turmoil, the protest, seemed to halt within her for a moment.

"We went to China. My sons and I left for China that year," said the woman. "We carried what we could of Frankfurt in our blood with us—its culture, its wisdom, its democratic history. Or perhaps the only thing we really took with us was the sound of Goethe's words saying many things to us who were also the German people, saying very clearly that wisdom's last decree is that freedom and life are deserved only by those who conquer them anew each day." The girl and the woman both finished the wine in their glasses, and the girl sat turning the glass in her fingers while opposite her the woman's voice went on speaking gently and patiently of a town that had been Frankfurt once, and a country that had been Germany. "That was a gift I had to give my children," the woman said; "a belief in free men which free men themselves had communicated to me."

And, as the girl listened to the woman's voice going on with this, the city they travelled toward took on another aspect, and the sound of the familiar German voices perished, no longer saying, as they had said to her for six months now: "I lost everything in the bombings, everything—my house, my furniture, my business," for the woman was speaking of the Taunus hills, and of the walks they had taken there in the springtime, she and the others, the professors, the artists, the writers, the free men of Frankfurt who had seen freedom die.

"And now you are going back? After fifteen years, you are going back?" the girl said, looking at her, and forgetting to turn the wine glass on the cloth.

"Yes," said the little woman. "No choice was offered. The women and children of foreigners were being evacuated. I was flown out of China last week. I am going back to Frankfurt," she said, the smile hanging on her mouth again, "because there does not seem any other place for me to go."

"How many children did you have?" the girl asked, for it was the members of this family which mattered, as the rest of Germany had never mattered. It was what they had been, and how they had spoken, and what answer they had given when the questions had been asked.

"I had four sons," the woman said, and her hand had begun to tremble again as she lifted her glass again to drink. "Two of them left Germany with me, the two younger ones. We went to China together," she said, having wet her lips with the wine. "The two others," she went on saying after a moment, but she could not go on with it at once. "The two others," she began again, and there was no hint of crying, nothing that even resembled anguish in the words she said. "The two others died with their countrymen and women in

Dachau," was what she was saying, but even the strength of
the wine she drank was not enough to lean on now, and her
lips, her chin, her empty hands, were trembling as if stricken
with the plague.

"Now it is my turn to order another half bottle," the girl
said quickly, and she made the sign to the waiter as he passed
with the *bombes glacées*. And then she reached across the
table, and she touched the woman's worn aged hand that lay,
like a forgotten object, on the cloth.

"I am afraid to go back," the woman said, and her teeth bit
hard into her shaking lip. "I am not afraid of my memories.
I am afraid of hearing what the living now have to say."

"We can listen to other things," the girl said, and their
hands held to each other's as the waiter set the plates of crack-
ers and cheese before them, and poured the fresh wine out.
And then the stooped little woman shouldered the burden of
patience and resignation again, and she smiled across the table
at the girl.

"I shall make out very well," she said, and their hands
drew apart, and they lifted their glasses and drank. "I have a
widow's pension accumulated at the university. It will be
enough to begin again on," she said, and an unsteady look
of recklessness or tipsiness came into her face. "It will be
enough to pay my way into the Palm Garden in the afternoons,
and there'll still be the orchid hothouse, with orchids as different as people, with wise faces, and foolish ones," she said, and
she giggled as if she were a young giddy woman now. "I
don't remember how many species there were, but I knew
them all by name once. And in the tropical conservatory,
there'll be the camellias flowering, reddish and white and

waxy, as they flowered in China so profusely—" And then she stopped talking. "Unless," she said quickly. "I mean, was the Palm Garden bombed—are the greenhouses there still?"

"Yes, they are there," said the girl, and then the two women began to laugh across the table at each other.

"I must write to my sons at once, to my two boys in China," the woman said, wiping the tears of laughter away, "and tell them how tall the banana trees have grown."

Cabaret

THE STAGE was small; it was no more than a platform impro-
vised at the far end of a long ground-floor room which had
been for three centuries a *Gaststube* in a small town in Land
Hesse. The *Gaststube* walls, ponderous with ancient wainscot-
ing and large mirrors framed in gilded wood, seemed now to
have set aside their own historical significance to converge toward the vanishing point at which the unseen actors were
about to play. The curtains were still drawn, and behind them
a half dozen of the young players waited in impatience, the
grease paint bright and porous on their faces, elated as children
are elated with their own wild, nearly incommunicable fervor,
taking turns at peering through one or the other of the two
holes which pierced the velvet curtains at the height of a man's

eye. To the townspeople who had put their good clothes on for an evening of entertainment and taken their places at the tables under the elaborate brass chandeliers, these holes were not perceptible, but to the restless group of players they were like windows opening upon life itself, each containing the exact measure of promise the evening held.

Among them was a girl in pink satin, lace-trimmed underwear, and if she had played Ophelia the night before, that was over and done with, for now she had coarsened into the professional female, with her limbs stripped naked, and her small untrembling breasts revealed as hard as rock within the yellow lace. Perhaps her jaw was too determined and businesslike for love, but still she was turned out in a traditional concept for its diversions, with high-heeled black satin mules on her bare, blue-veined feet, and rhinestone butterflies caught in the dark bush of her hair. And there was a long-necked boy with lank brown locks, in a velveteen jacket and a flowing tie, dressed to play the part of a poet; and a blond-haired youth in white linen shorts, and a T shirt, with the bronze of artificial sunburn glowing on his face and throat and forearms, as well as on his muscular calves and thighs. There was a man with a wealth of black whiskers, perhaps the curled black horsehair of mattress stuffing put to this use, with a fur cap on his head, and a bright red tunic tucked inside his trousers, who stood on tiptoe in his Cossack boots, seeking to see across the shoulders of the others into the *Gaststube,* with the hammer and sickle in metal crossed in the fur of his cap, and worn on his tunic, in the region of his heart. Another young woman stood in the group of them, a girl with narrow hips, and metal-colored hair, and a skin still tawny from the summer sun. From the sullen look of her mouth, and the weariness of her lids, it could be deduced that she had seen Dietrich play a role or two; and it may have been that her legs were as beautiful as Dietrich's, but only her broad shoulders, and her slim arms, and her smoothly knit bare back, were revealed in the long black sheath of satin which she wore.

But there was one dominant figure who stood taller than the rest of them—a young man in the shabby greatcoat of a Wehrmacht soldier, with the Wehrmacht cap, bearing a swastika, placed jauntily on his head. He was a bold young man, but in spite of the look of insolence in his eye, there was something else to him. There was vigor and drama in his bones, and a chronicle of suffering and deception was written in pride and intrepidity upon his face. On either side of his arrogant, humorous mouth there were scars marked deeply in his flesh, such as mark with bitterness the faces of those who have been disabled young, and who will have none of it.

"Petscher's using the upper half of his wife for a showcase tonight," he whispered sharply. He had shouldered aside whoever was in his way, and put one cold blue eye to a hole in the curtain, and he spoke with irony. "Advertising three watches on one side of her bust and a selection of fake gold cuff links on the other, all with the price tags hanging on them. Every article on display may be purchased at Petscher's, Marktplatz 21, open 9 a.m. until 5 p.m., Monday through Saturday," he said, and he stepped aside in impatience to let the poet see.

It was the Wehrmacht soldier who had conceived of the cabaret show they were about to give, and his was the voice that was ready to roar aloud the others' lines, as well as his own, if their courage failed them now. They were known for their Schiller, and Gorki, and Molière, and their Shakespeare was respected; but the performance on which the curtain was about to rise had nothing to do with the classics. It was their own, with the name of no other playwright signed to it; it was their commercial venture, for money they had to have. They had talked too long among themselves of Sartre, and Tennessee Williams, of Thornton Wilder, and Pirandello, of Camus, and Borchert, and Saroyan, speaking as intimately of these strangers as if they stood waiting their cues in the wings with them. The cue was money, and their palms were itching for it. They must have money in order to speak aloud with passion not only the lines of the classics, but a lingo contemporary enough to be taken for blasphemy in the hushed and darkened auditorium of a pompous country's defeat.

"The Schunk and Fiddemühle garage people have just come in," said the girl in the tight black satin sheath. Her eye, the lid of it smeared with blue salve, was fixed to the other hole in the curtain, and her voice was husky and low. "Frau Schunk in silver fox, and Frau Fiddemühle in ostrich feathers. You can get the stink of black-market gas on them from here," she said.

The Wehrmacht soldier put his hands on her naked shoulders, his touch professional, impersonal, as if his palms cupped nothing more living than metal or stone. And it could be seen that the two middle fingers of his right hand were missing, and that on the left there remained only the forefinger and thumb.

"Two tables empty still! I want the place filled up!" he whispered sharply, having moved the girl aside so that he might see. From beyond the curtain could be heard the murmuring of the spectators' voices, and the chiming of silverware, and china, and glass.

Below the platform, a pianist, a violinist, and a harpist had taken their places, and the pianist touched the keys softly, while the violinist and the harpist lowered their heads and tried their strings. And then, when the watches marked half past eight, the lights in the *Gaststube* were extinguished, and the three musicians played the introductory bars. The murmuring of the spectators ceased, the waiters no longer moved from table to table, but were lost in immobility in the shadows, and behind the curtains, on which the footlights cast their scallops of illumination, all but the Wehrmacht soldier hastened from the boards. He stood alone in the center of the stage, his head, with the beaked cap of the German Army on it, raised, his arms folded high across the breast of the long gray overcoat, waiting dramatically there while the sound of casual life was stilled. It was in this posture that the spotlight found him when the curtains parted—his hands thrust out of sight beneath his armpits, his brutal young mouth set, his greased lids masking nothing of the boldness of his eyes.

"You know my face? You have seen me before?" he asked the spectators. "You saw me at Stalingrad, you say? Yes, I was there!" His voice rang out across the *Gaststube* with a sound of violence, of profound excitement in it, which made a theatre of the place at once, and his word struck the brass of the chandeliers and the darkened panes of the mirrors like the flat of a castigating hand. The people to whom he had put the question had no interest left for the goblets of pink and yellow water-ice which the waiters had set before them, or for the flute-shaped glasses of white wine. "It was cold that winter! We were hungry, but there was nothing to put between our teeth except our bitterness! We ate our horses when they fell, and gnawed at the living when the cold had turned their carcasses to stone!" he said, and those at the tables who had taken their wafers up to eat them, put them down upon their plates again, and the Wehrmacht soldier lowered his voice to a whisper, and his eyes were bright and bold as he leaned across the footlights toward the tradespeople who had paid their money out for something advertised as a sensational cabaret. "Three hundred and thirty thousand men defending the frontiers of the Fatherland, defending our frontiers on the Volga!" he said in savage irony. "Do you remember Height 135, the Kasachi Hills, Gumrak, Tulevoy Ravine?" he whispered sharply. "Can you tell me how many hundreds of thousands of us, how many generations of us, died?" And now he freed his maimed hands from his armpits, but with a show of difficulty, as if drawing them from the grip of some powerful encumbrance which held them fast. He ran his right forefinger inside the collar of his coat, his mouth twisted as he gasped audibly for air or sustenance, turning his hand with skill so that no one might see the welt of flesh where the quick prehensile digits once had been. "Defeat!" he shouted in a choking voice. "Defeat! That was the sentence passed on us, and no reprieve! Defeat by cold, hunger, ground by the tread of tanks to rag and rot, screams throttled by the thumbs of death, eyes turned to ice before the tears could fall from them!"; saying it to them as husband, brother, or son, who would never return again might have said it before he died. The spectators sat uneasily upon the ancient straight-backed chairs, for now it was no longer a performer before them who mouthed written lines, but a manifestation of their own reality who spoke their rankling pain aloud. Those who had returned, lamed, broken, no more than stumps of men, had said it to them in words similar to these, so for a moment it seemed this was the voice of Germany itself which spoke to them across the footlights, and, sitting at the tables, they looked into one another's faces, and nodded quietly. And then, without warning, he betrayed them all, baring his teeth and spitting the taste of Germany's defeat across the boards. He stood erect again, his hands thrust into the pockets of his overcoat, his chin flung up. "Bombed out? Lost everything? Don't like the Occupation?" he cried, aping the whine. "Bah, the tune's been played three years too long! The notes are flat!" This was the signal for the musicians who sat below the platform to begin softly to play. "At Stalingrad I took an oath concerning that!" the Wehrmacht soldier said in his contempt for them. The mask of comedy was clapped onto his face now, and he strolled, in time with the music's tempo, back and forth across the stage.

"I swore if I survived to mime, to rant,
Lived to shoot boar and roebuck in their
season, study Hegel, Kant,
That I would split my sides with laughing!"

he said, speaking confidentially to them, and he broke the rhythm of his stanzas to throw his head back and give them a sample of that laughter at its best.

"The war that followed cold or hot,
The Germans unified or not,
Stalemate in Berlin, check at Bonn,
The West Mark battle lost or won,
Negotiations mostly black,
If I got back
From Stalingrad, I swore to laugh!"

And now his violent laughter rang across the *Gaststube* tables, and rattled through the chandeliers. He stood there with his head flung back upon his muscular throat, the white of his teeth and eyes, the bold blue of his lids, and the ochre of his make-up, embellished by the sphere of illumination in which he was contained as if in purest glass. His hands were laid against his belly, adroitly placed so that their mutilation might not be perceived, and the words he tried to speak were lost in the sound of his own loud shameless laughter, and in the spectators' laughter which spread, without their knowing why they laughed, from table to table in the crowded room.

> *"Let Occupation statutes wait*
> *While we enjoy our buffer fate!"*

he managed to roar out at last;

> *"For what's a state if not of mind,*
> *Bi-zone, tri-zone, or any kind?*
> *Whatever comes, there's Garry Davis,*
> *Who's absolutely sure to save us! Let's laugh!"*

he cried, the strength of his voice again drained by his laughter; and, as he bent double, crippled by his mirth, the people at the tables laughed until the tears came into their eyes.

With the laughter at its loudest, the musicians brought their music to its climax, and the curtains were drawn before the townspeople had time to recover and see the look of calculation in the convulsed actor's canny eye. *Twenty-eight tables,* he estimated rapidly, *seating four to eight persons each, makes an average of one hundred and sixty-four times the cover charge of D.M. 2, plus ten per cent of the refreshments, approximating possibly D.M. 1000 per night, if this continues for the two-week run.* The young, he thought savagely, buying our way back to decency again! You'll have Sartre and Camus to choke on when our new season begins! And when the curtains parted again, but an instant later, the Wehrmacht soldier was gone, and the stage was set for a bedroom scene, for things were moving quickly now. On the boards was a shabby divan, which had perhaps served as prop for thirty years or more, refurbished now with fancy lace-covered cushions; and behind the divan was a three-panelled screen of midnight blue, with a pair of black silk stockings flung across it; and beside the divan a night table on which stood a perfume atomizer, and a half-empty bottle of cognac, and an empty liqueur glass. On the divan itself reclined the barelegged, long-jawed young woman in her pink undergarments, the rhinestone butterflies enmeshed in her hair.

The musicians played "Tales of Hoffmann," with a ludicrous twist to the rendering of it, as if their tongues were in their cheeks, and the young woman lying on the divan stretched her firm white legs and arms and sang her aria of complaint. There were some in the audience who had seen her play Juliet or Ophelia in the weeks before, but all that was left of Juliet now was the look of the flesh designed for love, and all that remained of Ophelia was the repeated gesture of the arm and hand, not strewing flowers, but reaching for the perfume atomizer or the cognac bottle or the glass. For now she was "France," obscene, corrupt, degenerate, and a hazy reproduction of the Eiffel Tower had been painted in the window of the canvas backdrop so that there would be no mistake about her nationality. But she sang in German, spraying her bare chest and shoulders and the dark bush of her hair with perfume as she warbled of the Ruhr. Coal, coke, and steel was what she wanted in payment for her favors, as a lesser tart wanted jewels for her fingers and pelts for her back. She sang in German, but it was in French that she cried out in alarm when the blond young athlete in his white shorts and T shirt sprang through the window frame painted on the backdrop, effacing the Eiffel Tower for an instant as he came. Around his neck hung a string of American canned foods which clattered aloud as, with his jaws chewing steadily at a wad of gum, he hastened to her across the little stage.

"Mon dieu, c'est toi, Marshall?" the young woman cried out, and the tradespeople seated at the tables roared with laughter as he sought to take her in his strong bronzed arms. The young woman glanced uneasily toward the door, and at the window behind her, while the young man dropped on his knees before her, and, seeking to press his hand in passion on his heart, his fingers closed instead upon a can of Heinz's spaghetti in tomato sauce.

"Have you tried my Chinese dinner, boxed for four, complete with chopsticks and pigtail?" he pled with her, making this speech in English as he kneeled before her on the boards. "Or my Italian *pasta* which requires no cooking, seasoned with predigested Parmesan? Or my Danish eggs, with the tenderness of the hen frozen in? There's another treat in store for you!" he wooed her to the accompaniment of the necklace of cans. "Golden bananas dehydrated by camel drivers right on the desert and shipped to you with the money-back guarantee of twelve full ounces of desert sunlight sealed in each can, topped by true-to-life skins in a separate package, just add water, stitch the bananas securely inside, and, boy, you'll taste the tropics, you'll hear the throbbing heart of the jungle—"

"But, Marshall, I haven't a can opener!" the young woman cried out, and she poured the liqueur glass full again.

"There's one in every can of Alaskan minced clams!" the young man went on, still talking fast. "In fact, in each can of this superlative fish food, you will find a Shetland pony and cart, a fireless cooker, a 1949 Chevrolet, a television set, Hollywood, and a foreign agent just lifted from a key position in the State Department—" And now he must wait until the uproarious laughter had subsided at the tables before he could hope to be heard again. The spectators rocked on their chairs, or they shouted their laughter aloud, or else they pressed their handkerchiefs to their mouths to staunch it, their delight augmented by their knowledge that he had been a prisoner of war for three years in America and had learned this jargon at first hand, thus, in some fashion, having outwitted, and outwitting still, his captors by aping their idiom so viciously. "Get your atomic energy today the sure way!" he besought her, and he jumped up from his knees.

"Hush!" whispered the young woman, but she let him put his arms around her as she glanced furtively about. "Perhaps we aren't alone, *mein Schatz*," she said, and, as he snapped the elastic strap of her brassière upon her shoulder, the audience cried again in its exquisite pain.

The snapping of the brassière strap was the bewhiskered man's cue, and he emerged laboriously from under the divan, cursing, irate, shaking not one, but two fists in the air. And while the spectators howled at the sight of the scarlet tunic, and the hammer and sickle in such straits, the girl fled in her high-heeled black satin mules and her pink underwear around the table, with the young man in his shorts bounding after her, the string of cans he wore clattering and jumping as he ran. As he passed the night-table, he reached for the cognac bottle, to seize it up as weapon, but missed it in his panic and got the perfume atomizer instead. And now he raced on with it, spraying its contents at the bearded man who came lumbering behind him in pursuit.

"Veto! Veto!" shouted the man who ran as unwieldy as a bear, the fur cap slipped sideways on his head. It was he who managed to seize the cognac bottle by its neck, and he brandished it at the blond young man who leapt with agility before him a jump behind the half-clothed figure of the whore. "Veto! Veto!" cried the man in the red tunic, and he swung in his tracks to cut off the girl's retreat, and the fur cap flew from his head. At the sight of him standing with his arms wide open, the young woman turned too, and ran, the symbol of a country whose name was pain to every German in the room, but who now pretended as they laughed that France was not the unpaid debt, the unhealed wound, but merely a vulgar woman in her underwear. This they can take, thought the Wehrmacht soldier, standing in the wings, and hearing the laughter in the hall. This they can fool themselves with for a little while, until the rest of it comes!

And so they were off again, the girl on her high heels still in the lead, racing in single file past the reproduction of the Eiffel Tower, the three of them disappearing behind one end of the screen and coming out the other, the tin cans clattering, the atomizer spraying, the musicians below the platform playing faster and faster, neck and neck in tempo with the actors' pace. "Veto! Veto!" spluttered the man in his doused red tunic as the cologne water filled his mouth and eyes and nose. At the height of this pandemonium, with the chandeliers quivering on their antique stems and laughter rocking the place, the velvet curtains were drawn closed.

The next skit was as tranquil as a summer field: three pretty young women with aprons tied around their waists, and their hair worn in shining plaits, stood hand in guileless hand upon the stage, and recited, in childlike trebles, their seemingly naive couplets concerning the monetary reform. One girl in Hessian peasant dress, represented the Reichsmark, another, in Bavarian costume, the Deutschmark, and the third, the East Zone mark, with a beribboned Slavic headdress crowning her serene broad brow. The townspeople could eat and drink at ease to this accompaniment, even signal to the waiters for more wine, laugh circumspectly, and clap with moderation when the curtains closed. But the skit which followed on the heels of this was something else again: the girl in the black satin sheath stood there alone, one languorous hand placed on her slender, sloping hip, as striking as Dietrich herself to them, metallic-haired and glamorous in the clear cone of the spotlight on the darkened stage. The music played softly, with yearning, below her, and her greased lids were heavy, her long emerald eyes seemingly drugged with dreams or memories of love. She sang of this country that was theirs, of the cities that were rubble, and of the people who lived in the cellars and craters that remained. And, as she sang, her low husky voice was bitter, and the words were half crooned, half snarled in passion, while she moved in insolence and indolence, her hips weaving slowly, across the boards.

"Bathtubs hang by their piping from second stories still," she sang in her sultry German to them, "and bedroom doors swing on their hinges, opening forever now upon eternity! Staircases end in space, the last flight gone, and moss upon them, but our hearts run down them still in memory! Out of the débris where once a city stood, a vine writhes upward through a fallen statue's hand, two swallows build their nest on a church altar laid open to the rain, a tree grows tall and flowers through a schoolroom's broken heart, where children played who'll never play again!" Out of these ruins, this rubble, she snarled at the people in the *Gaststube*, love, or some imitation of it, had crawled like a rat, had slithered in hunger and desire from the moonlit stones. "Girls," she drawled huskily, making the word a long vicious caress, "came one by one, came two by two, and walked the streets in search of it," and she moved slowly, sinuously, across the stage. "Girls buttoned their worn jackets tight!" she cried out in grim pity for them. "Girls lingered on street corners like alley cats, accosted the living with their hearts sick for the dead!"

And, as she sang, the girls, almost identically dressed, came one by one and two by two from the wings, and they strolled with lagging steps past the ruins which took tentative shape now on the canvas backdrop. They wore plaid wool skirts, and bright plastic shoulder-strap bags, and saddleback shoes, and nylon stockings, and all they wore was recognizable as that mail-order-house merchandise which had become standard apparel for the *Fräuleins* of the American Zone. There were six or eight of them, moving like shadows against the shadowy ruins which served as background to the single figure in her monocle of light. Their singing began with a drowsy humming in the throat, and, as if following their lead, the musicians below them found the notes upon their instruments, and the young woman, swaying to the rhythm of it, drawled huskily, and with contempt, the words the audience knew well.

138

"Johnny, *wenn Du'ne Kamel hast*," she sang, and cigarettes appeared, whether Camels or not, in the hand of every sauntering girl; "*bin ich bei Dir zu Gast*," it went, and the minute separate wings of illumination fluttered briefly in the darkness as each girl paused, with the music's beat, and struck a match, and bent her head, and drew the first breath in. And then they strolled aimlessly, idly, on again, humming the tune at the same lingering pace at which they walked. "Johnny, *wenn Du'ne Kamel hast*," went the words as the girl sauntered past the moonlit ruins, "I'll spend the whole—long—night—with —you!"

The applause was such that they must do a portion of their act again, with the girl who might have been Dietrich speaking their intention as she swayed before them, muscular, savage, slender, in her tight black dress. And then the curtains were drawn closed, the lights came on in the *Gaststube* chandeliers, and the musicians got to their feet and made their way out to the entrance where draughts of cool night air came through the opened doors. This was the intermission, and when the girl, her flesh shining with grease paint and sweat, stepped into the wings, the Wehrmacht soldier, who had discarded his uniform now for the part that was to come, put his quick strong hands upon her naked shoulders, and drew her savagely against him.

"My God, we've put it over!" he said.

"The *Herr Kulturreferent* is giving us two columns in tomorrow's paper!" cried the symbol of France, no longer in her underwear, and she beat the Wehrmacht soldier on the back. "Three tables have ordered the best champagne! The management is trying to get ice!"

"Wait," said the blond girl huskily, her curved, clinging body stirring under the Wehrmacht soldier's hands. "No one sitting out there at the tables has come in for criticism yet."

"What should we wait for? Censure?" the soldier cried out, his whisper loud, and reckless, and gay. He wore a local conception of American democratic dress: gray flannel trousers, which had not recently been cleaned or pressed, striped shirt, striped tie, and a shapeless brown felt hat pushed to the back of his head. And now he dropped his hands from the girl's shoulders, and he turned to manipulate the backdrop depicting the city ruins away across the boards. With him labored the poet, still dressed for the poet's role, and the bearded man, no longer in a tunic or with a fur cap on his head, but wearing an ancient black frock coat, and trousers that tapered to gaiters buttoned over the split leather of his shoes. "Listen to them snapping their fingers for more wine out there, maybe even for beefsteaks!" the Wehrmacht soldier said, speaking of these others as if more than a length of curtain divided actors from audience, and as he and the poet and the bearded man shifted the scenery in the heat, the sweat stood on their brows.

And then the blond young man, no longer in white shorts or with a necklace of tin cans around his neck, maneuvered the backdrop of a stately university building out of the wings and into place.

"*Herr Oberstaatsanwalt* Jauernick has made reservations for twenty-five for Saturday night!" he said, his voice hoarse with effort. He was wearing knee-high boots now, and shirt and trousers of military cut, and of a familiar brown. On his right sleeve could be seen an insignia done in black and white, and circled with red, in size and shape and from a distance deceptively like the one the world had cause to know. But in-

stead of a hooked cross within the circle, there was the head
of a sheep, done in white on black, with one ear up and one
ear down. "If we want to make money, perhaps we shouldn't
go too far," he said.

"Too far?" cried the Wehrmacht soldier, and he straightened up and pushed the American felt hat back further on his
head. "We're just halfway! Do you want us to back down
now?"

"If they walk out tonight, the whole thing will be off," said
the blond young man in his shirt and trousers of military cut,
and he looked at the others uneasily.

"When a miser is played on the stage, does the miser in the
audience recognize himself?" the Wehrmacht soldier roared
in his impatience with them.

"Then what's the use in playing it out?" said the poet,
speaking scarcely aloud.

"We could do the one on dying British aristocracy instead,"
said the bearded man in the frock coat. The vacillation in his
voice had nothing to do with his height or his breadth or the
show of whiskers on his face, and he set to brushing the dust
of the boards from his rusty black in order not to meet the
Wehrmacht soldier's eye.

"By God!" he cried out, and he swung on his heel, and he
jerked the felt hat forward with his mutilated right hand. "By
God!" he said again, and then he made the rest of it sound
humorous. "Have you forgotten? We're playing for posterity!"

But the skit which followed immediately after was harm-
less enough. It was certainly not the one which the evening
had been leading up to, word by word, and line by line. It was
played by the bearded man in his gaiters and frock coat, and

the Wehrmacht soldier in his American clothes, and the poet
with his velveteen jacket and his soft silk tie. They disagreed
in couplets, and in rhyme as well as song—the typical *Herr
Professor* of a provincial town, and the typical poet-philosopher, and the typical collaborationist whose tradition dated
since 1945, speaking sometimes in chorus, sometimes sepa-
rately. The *Herr Professor* maintained that super-learning
should be dispensed by super-pedagogues exclusively, and
only to super-super-alumni in super-scientific fields. As he
stepped a minuet with dignity, holding the tails of his frock
coat like a skirt in his two hands, he stated the consensus of
academic opinion was that those who were merely the sons or
grandsons of college graduates could hardly qualify for entry
into university. They must be the great-grandsons of university
scholars, or else the super-standards set by super-precedent
would suffer, he asserted, and the ideal of super-erudition
be lost. The poet-philosopher deplored the infiltration of
foreign influence into the national arts, and his voice was
languid, weary, as he ran his fingers through his lank hair.
He did a turn or two of a swooning waltz, complained of
television from America, existentialism from France, and
barbarism from the East, then leaned against the backdrop for
support, describing himself, and nearly collapsing beneath the
weight of it, as the standard bearer of culture for the Western
world.

But it was the Wehrmacht soldier in his gray flannel trousers
and striped shirt who made them rock with laughter again.
He stood with the felt hat pushed to the back of his head, and
a chewed cigar in one corner of his mouth, explaining the
ethics of collaboration in a rapid, nasal twang. Yes, sure, he
worked with the *Amis*, he said; he liked the way they kept

their feet on the desk during office hours. It saved shoe leather, and you had to take things like that into consideration, with the price the stores were asking for shoes now.

"Sure, I work with the *Amis*," he sang in a nearly perfect imitation of American, and he jitterbugged expertly to the music, his hands kept out of sight, his teeth still chewing the cigar. "They don't have Coca Cola in the Eastern Zone!" he sang. "They don't have Primadoras in Moscow!"

And then this skit was over, and the stage set for the final scene. For a moment, after the curtains parted, there was silence in the *Gaststube*, for nothing was there before the spectators except the blankness of the backdrop and the empty boards. There was nothing for the eye or mind to fasten on, or for the ear to hearken to, until the cadence of marching began off stage. At first it was a mere light tattooing, as if the feet were coming from a long way off, and then, as the piano and violin and harp began to play the martial music, the volume of its sound increased, coming louder, and even louder now, out of the wings. And, as it grew, the rhythmic pulsating seemed to fill the *Gaststube*, beating not only upon the ears but striking its tempo on the flesh as well, oppressing them, crowding them, like a gigantic throbbing heart closed in the *Gaststube* with them, stopping the air in their nostrils, the speech in their mouths.

Then came the men and women, dressed similarly in brown, wearing knee-boots, and with the deceptive insignia on their sleeves, marching in from both sides of the platform in single file, and there they about-faced, and came to a halt, their feet still marking time. There were perhaps no more than five or six of them on either side, but they appeared to be more numerous as they stood with chins raised and muscles rigid, in the cramped space of the stage. They held themselves with singular intensity, as if the eyes of the entire world were fixed on them; and it may have been that the eyes of the entire world were on them, watching in apprehension every gesture these young people made. Two of the men could be recognized as waiters who had served at the *Gaststube* tables not ten minutes before, recruited because of the shortage of male players, and marking time with the others on the boards. But it was not this which caused the first titter of laughter to run through the room. The thing which set it off was the recognition of another figure, one wearing the brown uniform as well, who came limping down the human corridor of men and women whose boots still marked the time and temper of an epoch that was past. He wore the official beaked cap, with the crown exaggeratedly high above the brow, and under one arm he carried an outsized portfolio. Now that he paused downstage, before the footlights, his title could be seen written plainly out in Gothic letters upon the leather, so no mistake could possibly be made concerning his identity. *"Propagandaminister für den Reiksschleisskreitzer,"* it said, and the spectators glanced at those seated at the other tables before they tittered at the outrageous name.

"Halt!" barked the poet, cast now in the Propaganda Minister's role, and on the stage the double row of boots ceased instantly to move.

"Baa-aa!" responded the uniformed men and women in a single docile voice. They stood, their eyes upon him, giving him an incredible salute. It did not consist of the arm raised stiffly as of old, but of the thumb being pressed to the tip of the nose, and the fingers of that hand wagged at him in apparent gravity.

And now the tradespeople, dressed up in their best clothes, sat uneasily at the tables, startled a moment by the shamelessness of it, but entranced by the very indecency of what they saw. Even those who had believed in it all once did not rise from their seats and walk in protest from the room, but instead they resorted to laughter. And, having laughed, they seemed relieved, as if they had broken a mirror set before them, and now it could no longer bear their completed image, but only fragments of it, on its glass. When the Propaganda Minister made his absurd address, they laughed as people will who have taken a long time to see the point of a story which other people consider funny, and who laugh all the louder to cover their own stupidity. Or perhaps it was because of the amount they had drunk that they were ready to laugh now at whatever took place upon the boards, but, however it was, they roared in anticipation when the Propaganda Minister announced that the *Reiksschleisskreitzer* himself was about to appear, and they laughed the louder when a housepainter, in the traditional paint-bespattered, white cotton suit, balancing a ladder on one shoulder and a bucket of paint hung over his arm, made his way from the wings.

The young men and women in uniform cried "Baa-aa!" in homage to him, and, as he fought his way with difficulty up the corridor they formed, the swinging ends of the ladder walloped first one and then the other, nearly knocking them off their feet, and the onlookers laughed louder in their savage joy. They watched him set the bucket of paint down, and then seek to set the ladder against the backdrop, working with that sidesplitting, clumsy concern with which a clown prepares his act. Once the ladder was upright and wavering uncertainly behind him, he stooped for the bucket of paint again, and it could be seen that there were two fingers missing from his hand. And now he began to mount the ladder, testing its balance step by step, while the men and women on the stage stood at attention, and bleated their exalted "Baa-aa!" When he was at the top, and wavering precariously there, he turned his back upon the audience and began to slap the dripping brushfuls of white paint out. "Slap!" went the brush across the backdrop, and a shower of white paint fell on the men and women and the Propaganda Minister below. "Slap!" went another brushful, and despite the fact that their uniforms were splattered with it, they raised their voices in another fervent "Baa-aa!"

At least, all the voices except one, which suddenly called out: "Boo!"

"Execute him! See that his widow gets no pension and doesn't collect his life insurance!" barked the Propaganda Minister, and the spectators roared anew as hands reached from the wings and jerked the offender from the stage.

The *Reiksschleisskreitzer* swung perilously around now on the ladder, and he began his speech to the uniformed men and women and to the *Gaststube* as he slapped the paint out wildly on the empty air. The spectators were prepared to laugh at all of it; they only asked that the words, and the pitch of the voice, be familiar enough to them so that they could hold their aching sides and writhe upon their seats. For what was he but the point of a colossal joke that history had played upon the world, the burlesque of a man some other people had chosen as their leader once at some other time and in some other place? This was someone they had no use for any longer, for he had deceived them into believing he would succeed in what he had set out to do. There would be another, a better one soon, who would give them back their pride.

"For decades now we have been oppressed, we have been treated like taxpayers!" he cried out, slinging the paint across the stage. "But if today we are allowed only twenty-five thousand housepainters, I tell you by 1951 we shall have fifty thousand housepainters, regardless of whether we have any houses!" he shouted, and he painted the picture of the future in reckless dripping strokes on empty space. "And in 1954, we shall have a hundred and fifty thousand housepainters, and in 1956, one million nine hundred and fifty thousand house-painters!" he cried, his voice rising higher, the words coming faster, the ladder swaying more wildly as the numbers rose. "And in 1958, we shall have five million five hundred and fifty thousand housepainters!" he cried, and the men and women in uniform wiped the paint from their eyes and their mouths, and in one voice shouted "Baa-aa!" "In 1960, we shall have fifteen million housepainters!" he was telling them now, his own voice rising to a scream as they bleated: "Baa-aa, baa-aa, baa-aa!" "In 1962!" the *Reiksschleisskreitzer* shrieked, and then the ladder gave its final oscillation beneath him, and the Propaganda Minister, limping and skipping and jumping to his aid, received the bucket of white paint square upon his head, and the *Gaststube* rocked with laughter as the *Reiks-schleisskreitzer* and the ladder fell.

This was the end of the performance, but not of the cabaret, which was obliged to prolong its scheduled three-week run. Ten additional tables were somehow moved onto the *Gast-stube* floor, but still there was not place enough for all. Those who had been there once would return a second, and even a third time, reminding one another that this kind of political satire had long been popular with the metropolitan German public, saying, with gratification, that it was too European, too informed, as entertainment to have any place in American night clubs or music halls. They came back, the tradespeople and the professional people of this town, and of the towns near it, to see the take-offs on the *Amis,* and the Russians, and the French, and to hear a German woman sing bitterly of love. And perhaps some of them returned for the last act alone, to close their eyes in the darkness, and drink their wine, and wait for the sound of the voice that cried higher and higher to the rhythmic pulsing of the feet.

Home

Now it was evening, and the rain had been falling all day, falling steadily on the ruins and rubble of the city, and the wind had been driving in hard from the outlying hills. It was the time of day to turn toward home, and a sadness seemed to fall, with the rain, upon the city streets, as if, at this hour, the entire city had come quietly to recognize the reason for its physical destruction, and the burden of its nearly unatonable sin. People whose daily work was done moved out of the doorways of the half-broken buildings, the shop-blinds descended, shuddering aloud, and the ferment of sale and barter came to a close. The streetcars came, riding the weather as a ship rides the sea, so filled with dark, clinging forms that they no longer

stopped for those who waited, but rocked on toward the out-
skirts of the German city, their bells clanging out in warning
through the falling rain.

It was only when you had come uptown as far as the American Shopping Center that the grief and longing which beset
the city seemed to be assuaged. Here the Army Post Exchange, and the Clothing Store, and the Coffee Shop, with its
ice-cream soda fountain, were emblazoned with neon lights,
and music came through amplifiers planted, like giant con-
volvulus, in the roof garden's illuminated shrubbery. There
were elegant cars parked cheek by jowl still in the cemented
drive before the buildings, for it was Wednesday, and the
Shopping Center closed an hour later on that day. The whole
place was set aside from ordinary life by seeded triangles of
grass, bordered by hedges, and these and the shrubbery
seemed artifically colored, but it was the rain and the flood-
lights which had painted them in phony green.

Here there was the constant, insouciant fluxing of the civilian and the military—the dependent children in their Gene
Autry outfits, with rodeo holster and pistol sets strapped at
their waists, and the groups of blue-jeaned high-school students passing, with their saddleback shoes, their insignia-
stamped windbreakers, giving this the cleavage of any Stateside town. Or there were the dependent wives in long, vividly
colored, mail-order-house coats, with the plaid-lined hoods of
them covering their silky hair, walking under the rain with
their husbands in uniform beside them, the captains and majors
and colonels carrying five-cent paper shopping bags by their
string handles as they pushed in and out of the bright, fanning
doors. While through the amplifiers which yawned above their
heads in this alien country, a voice they had known since time

began sang the familiar words of love aloud to them, keeping the sound of Germany away.

But there were men alone among these others, G.I.s come this far from barracks in the streetcars or by jeep, on a Wednesday evening, boys from the Southern states, or from the North, or from the West, or from the East, some with black skins and some with white, come for the sake of a Coke, or a banana split, or for the familiar layout of a newsstand; or come merely to sit, in their khaki socks, in the stalls of the "Wile-U-Wait'" shoe repair salon, to close their eyes, and dream there as they waited for new Catspaw heels to be affixed; come in loneliness to this lighted island which could not be accepted as home, but which might be taken for a little while as home's facsimile. One of these was a colored G.I. from Mississippi, with a month's pay in his pocket, who walked quickly toward the show windows of the Clothing Store, his head lowered into the springtime wind. It was the presence of someone waiting in the shadows of the building which stopped him as abruptly as if the darkness had pronounced his name.

"Why, hello," he said, and he lingered there, his hands thrust into his pockets out of the wet, his eyes seeking to make out the figure through the rain and the obscurity. "Hi, there," he said, speaking softly, as man might have said it to woman in his loneliness, but the figure gave no sign that it had heard. The soldier stepped closer to the border hedge, and he leaned across the budding twigs of it, and now he could see that the creature who waited there was no larger than a child, a child perhaps stricken to immobility and silence by the amplified music, and the hastening people, and by the neon lights which spelled their undecipherable message out. "What you think you doing out on a night like this one?" he said, and the child,

151

or the dwarf, or whatever it was that had taken shelter there, took the four or five intervening steps across the triangle of slipping, unseen mud, and made its way expertly through the brittle hedge. When it stood beside him on the pavement, the soldier laid his hand gently, in diffidence, on its shoulder, and he drew it forward with him toward the show windows of the Clothing Store. And there, in the two great golden squares of light cast out, he saw that his fingers touched the wool of a drenched gray sweater that stretched, ravelling, across the bare flesh of a boy of four or five. "You sure got yourself good and wet all over," the soldier said, and he paused, hesitant a moment, before looking shyly into the boy's face, perhaps fearing the record of want and hunger that might be written there.

"*Kalt*," the little boy said, and he looked up at the soldier, his cheeks as full and firm as a baby's cheeks, and even a look of impudence, of humor, in his long-lashed, lively eyes.

"You got no call to be cold this time of year," the soldier said, but here, out of the shelter of the building, he too felt the wind driving sharply in upon them from the springtime hills. He could feel the good covering of flesh on the boy's bones, for the clothes the boy wore were as thin as paper, and the bones under the covering of flesh were shaking in the soldier's hand. "You just went and got yourself so wet that it'd take a month to dry you out. That's all the matter with you. You just needs to get in where it's dry," the soldier said, and he looked around for a couple of other words to say, but he couldn't find them, for he had come only a few weeks before to this country, and the language of home was the only one that made any sense at all.

He kept one hand on the boy's shoulder, and like this they walked into the light of the entranceway together, walked with the high-school girls, and the dependent wives, and the military, toward where a German girl, with an officially be-ribboned badge pinned on her blouse, stood checking civilians at the swinging door. It may have been that she did not see beyond the soldier's uniform, and, seeing it, she did not put the question; or it may have been that, in the fluxing tide of women and men, she did not see the German boy go past. And once inside, the boy and the soldier stood motionless together, drawn suddenly apart from all the others, and, in his uneasi-ness, the soldier took his leather-beaked hat from the black curls on his head. Beyond hung a mirror, and, when the tide of white people parted, the soldier saw himself, tall, gaunt, chalk-eyed, separated not only by his color from these others, but by his own perplexity; and then, as if recalling that he had been lent a temporary dignity by the uniform he wore, he put his hat quickly back upon his head again. He stood hold-ing to the shoulder of the German boy, seeking to get his bearings in the confusion, to steer a course between the display of nylon nightgowns, and the Roy Rogers sweaters in primal colors, and the gaudily striped ties; while the others, with pur-pose and destination established in them, passed from counter to counter, come here for something they knew the size and shape and terms of, and which they would discard if the specifications were not the right ones, not come for the sake of warmth or light or an illusion of security. In the full-length panel of the glass, he could see that below the German boy's ravelling sweater hung shrunken cotton pants, and below the pants, ribbed, cotton stockings, black with wet, were twisted on his short, strong legs. But whatever shoes the boy had on his feet, the soldier could not make out, because of the ac-cumulated mud they bore.

"You had ought to wiped your feet off before you come in," the soldier said. The tide of people had closed again before the mirror, and the soldier looked down at the boy, and he saw that the fair hair was not cropped close to his head as he had seen it on the skulls of other German children, but it hung silky and long behind his ears and on his soiled small neck, and strands of it curled up fine and golden across his rain-wet brow.

"You Have Only One Mother," said a sign hanging over the silverware counter, and a wreath of forget-me-nots had been hand-painted around these simple words. "You Have Only One Mother" was written in white, perhaps in soap, in a flowing hand on the three-panelled glass at the lingerie counter, and the striped shower curtains in the Gift Shop Corner bore this same factual statement concerning Mother's Day. And it was the boy's eye or mind which cleared before the soldier's, and which singled out of the bright, animate confusion, the portrait of a woman's thin, sombre face. It was framed in pleated gilt paper, and it hung above the hosiery counter, where the stockings were shown drawn over shapely, wooden legs. There were legs which reclined on cushions, and others which did not, and above them meditated the stern censorious features of someone as recognizable as Whistler's mother, only the boy and the soldier had no way of knowing the features either of Whistler's, or his mother's, face.

"*Grossmütter!*" the boy cried out in his high, clear, impudent voice, and his fingers pulled at the soldier's sleeve. "*Grossmütter!*" he cried, with a kind of humor in it, and he pointed up at the woman with her thin lips and her meekly parted hair.

"Well, what d'y' know?" said the soldier, and a sense of wonder and pleasure came into his blood.

But for all their incongruity here, it might have been that the Clothing Store had been expecting them to come, for at the far end of its galleries a special counter had been prepared. Through the flux of shoppers, the soldier saw a pair of child's-size, calf's-hide cowboy boots set on the glass, and a black rubber coat, with a matching fireman's hat, standing high on the doll-like, smiling model of a boy.

"Looks like they're selling things for boys over there," the soldier said, and the boy in his ravelling sweater moved forward with him, his hand holding to the soldier's hand.

The German woman behind the counter might have stepped out of a schoolroom for the moment, taken refuge here from the uproariousness of the young and heedless, and now she straightened the ribbons of the official badge which labelled her one of the chosen, and she settled the pins in her knot of graying hair.

"Can I help you?" she said in her good imitation of American, but the soldier did not seem to see her standing there. Instead, he saw the cowboy boots on the glass pane of the counter, and he picked them up, and he looked at the soles of them, and at the heels, as carefully as if he had stood like this in stores at home with a blond-headed child beside him, and had learned what qualities you had to look for in the shoes that child would wear.

"Oh, *prima, prima!*" the boy cried out in his eagerness.

"Can I show you something?" the German woman said.

Behind her were the shelves with boys' shirts lying folded one upon the other in them, and boys' corduroys, boys' pull-

155

overs, and boys' blue jeans, with the smell of their denim, strong, familiar, like the smell of home upon the air. "If He's Yours, He Deserves the Best," the slogan was written above the shelves, and the soldier felt his own lips shaping the words of this unprecedented statement, his tongue moving slowly, cautiously, emitting no sound. Then he turned to the raincoat on the model, and his fingertips lifted the hem of it, and he looked at the lining, and then he let it fall, and with his open palm he stroked the fireman's black, sloping hat. His month's pay had gone so heavy with promise in his pocket now that he could scarcely bear the weight of it, and when the woman behind the counter spoke to him, he slowly brought himself to hear.

"Yes, ma'am," he said, and he took off his hat before her. And then he remembered the uniform he wore, and he put it on again. "There're pretty nice things you got here, ma'am," he said. It was not until then that he saw the felt slippers the boy had on his feet, with the toes thrusting, pale as putty, through them, having thrust through the ribbed stockings a long time before. "I want the best pair of shoes you got in the store for my little boy here," he said.

Behind the counter was a half circle of hinged, shoe-store seats, and the boy sat tentatively on the edge of the one the saleswoman pulled down for him, and then he slipped off it, and let it clap back into place again. He did this twice, and each time he did it, he looked around laughing, because of the slap of sound it made. His hair was drying in the heat of the store, and its color lightening, and his full, babyish cheeks were pressed up until his eyes were almost closed with laughing, and a flush spread over his soiled, merry face. The saleswoman had spoken in English to him, and not until she had sat down before the boy, and put out her hand to take the measurement, did she see the sodden, broken slippers, and her bent body straightened on the shoe-clerk's stool.

"Why, this is a German boy. He's German," she said, and she looked up in shocked rebuke.

"Well, yes, ma'am," said the soldier. "He's German. I found him standing outside the door."

"Germans are not allowed to come in here," the saleswoman said.

"Well, maybe neither him nor me's allowed to come in here," said the soldier, speaking gently, "but he's got the right to have shoes on his feet the same as you and me got the right."

Now that he sat back in this adult seat, the boy's legs were too short to bend at the knee, and they thrust out straight before him, like the legs of an unjointed doll. And once the saleswoman had taken his slipper off, and held it in distaste between forefinger and thumb, the boy began to talk in his high, almost impudent voice to her, or to anyone who would listen, piping wildly and sweetly of the cowboy boots, it may have been, or the raincoat, or the other things he wanted for his own. But however many elegant, clean pairs of shoes the saleswoman brought out, they would not go onto his feet because of the welts and the wet of the ragged stockings on his legs.

"I think you'll have to put dry socks on him first," the saleswoman said, and she held the new shoes in her hand, her eyes, her very being, withdrawn, making no move to peel his stockings away. "We have some cheap ones," she said, for she had been chosen by the Americans to serve Americans, and it was to them she gave her allegiance now. "We have some at twenty-five cents a pair."

"Maybe you got some better ones," the soldier said. "Maybe you got some that cost more." The saleswoman got up, and she set the shoes down on the floor, and she turned to study the numbers on the cartons on the shelves. Then she slid out the box marked "7," and she sat down again on the stool before the boy. In the box there were socks with multi-colored stripes, and others with flowered borders, and still others in solid blue, and solid red, and green, and gold. "Ask him what's his favorite color ma'am, will you?" said the soldier, his voice modest and shy.

When the saleswoman spoke to the boy in this tongue they shared in common, the bright, quick chattering came to a pause, and then, when she had finished, the boy began to slide back and forth on the hinged wooden seat again, speaking his high, sweet vocabulary of joy.

"He says he likes them all," said the saleswoman, resigned now to anything that they might say or do. "He says he wants them all."

"Well, that's O.K. with me. Tell him that's O.K.," the soldier said, and perhaps because he believed there might be some doubt in her mind concerning how much he had, the soldier took the bills of scrip from his pocket, and he began counting them carefully out. But she didn't want the money then; she wanted something else of him, and, seated there on the stool before the boy, she did not look at the soldier, but in spite of the shame, and the broken pride, which held and warped her spirit, she could not bring herself to take the rotted, black stockings from the boy's soiled legs. So the soldier stooped, and he pulled the boy's stockings off, and now that his feet were naked before them, they saw the inch or more of bleached, spongy flesh which cushioned the soles of the boy's feet. "Why, this boy's feet must have been frozen some time," the soldier said, the grief of it stabbing his heart. "Maybe not this winter, but a long time ago. But they was certainly frozen some time. Maybe when he was nothing but a baby lying in his crib," he said, and he held the boy's feet cradled in his long, dark hands.

It was while he picked out the shoes for the boy, and selected the underwear for him, and three bright shirts, and two pairs of blue jeans, and a printed neck-scarf with jewel nailheads and a bucking broncho in the pattern of it, and a nickel slide loop to draw it tight beneath the collar, that the soldier dreamed the brief, clear dream of love about the boy. For the duration of the dream, the boy was his, the authority of family, of country, of Occupation even, having discarded him; and the soldier, who had known only leaning Negro shacks, became the provider, the protector at last, the dispenser of white-skinned charity. There seemed to be no one in the American store now except the three of them, and no sound in their universe except the shrill, rapid piping of the boy. Then the soldier lifted the calf's-hide boots off the counter again, and he said: "He ought to have these to change to when he's done got the others wet." So he put the cowboy boots aside, with the shirts, and the blue jeans, and the underwear, and his fingers returned to the hem and the lining of the raincoat on the smiling pink-faced model of a child. "Maybe you got this in his size, and the hat that comes with it," the soldier said, but the boy was saying something to the woman. "What's that boy saying now?" the soldier said.

"He says his mother will be pleased," said the saleswoman, her voice acrid as she took her sales pad up. Over the hosiery counter the sign said: "You Have Only One Mother," and

"You Have Only One Mother" the runner above the silver-ware counter repeated, and Whistler's mother looked down on them, giving no quarter to man or boy as she eyed them from the pleated gilt paper of her frame.

"Would you ask him something for me, ma'am?" said the soldier, and his fingers on the raincoat ceased to move. "Would you ask him where his mother is?" he said.

The boy had got the wet gray sweater off alone, and he was struggling now to get his arms into the red and orange cow-boy shirt. When the saleswoman put the question to him, he was doing his best to get the buttons closed. He looked up at her with a marvelous brightness, a singular eagerness of lip, and tongue, and eye, but once she had heard his quick, in-souciant answer, the woman shook her head.

"He says he doesn't know where his mother is," she told the soldier, and then she turned away to look for the raincoat, and the fireman's hat, in the size the boy would wear. "That's the way things are in Germany now," she said in a wild, wounded voice when she came back to the counter. "Will there be anything else?" she said, and she took up her pencil and began writing the sales check out.

"Well, then, maybe you'd ask him whereabouts he lives," the soldier said.

The boy was doing the buttons of the shirt up wrong, and the soldier sat down on the hinged seat beside him, and his own long, supple fingers set the buttons right. Then he helped him pull the blue jeans on over the wet, shrunk, cotton pants, and he adjusted the straps of them over the boy's shoulders, while the woman put the second question to the boy.

"He says he doesn't know where he lives," she said in answer, saying these words in condemnation of him and of the people from which he came, her voice grim, relentless, in its yearning for the decency, the order, they had, as a country, known before.

The soldier was fixing the jeweled neck-scarf on the boy's shirt collar, adjusting the nickel slide loop of it, and for a moment he did not speak.

"Well, maybe you'd be so kind to ask him, ma'am, how he come here alone," the soldier said then, and the saleswoman turned her head toward the boy, but not quite to him, giving only the side of her schoolmistress face to him, and she put the words in a tense, low, almost menacing German to him, and at once, when she was finished, the eager piping of the boy's voice began.

And then his answer was given, and the saleswoman did not speak. She had begun making figures on the sales slip, but now her hand which held the pencil ceased to move, and she seemed to look at nothing, not at the sales pad before her, or at the people moving past the counter, or at the soldier, or the boy.

"He says his mother brings him here in the morning," she said at last, "and she leaves him outside when the people start coming. And then she comes back and picks him up in the evening again."

The soldier had arranged the neck-scarf on the boy's shirt, and he had finished with the buttons, and he sat without moving on the hinged wooden seat, unable to think of anything to say. And then his eyes shifted to the saleswoman's face, and before he spoke, he cleared his throat.

"Maybe he'd tell you if he was in here before—you know, if he ever come in with anybody who got things for him before he come in with me," he said.

The boy was dressed in the rodeo shirt, and the blue jeans,

and good tie-shoes were on his feet, and, as he spun in wonder before the full-length panel of the mirror, he did not hear the question the first time she put it to him. She had to say it twice before he halted in his spinning and the answer came.

"He says he's been in the P.X., and in the Coffee Shop, but nobody took him to the Clothing Store before," the saleswoman translated in bitterness. "He says somebody brought his little sister in last week, but the shoes she got weren't as good as the shoes you bought him, and she only got one pair of socks." Then she cried out in a low, fierce voice across the counter to the soldier: "Don't you see how it is with the people of this country? Don't you see they don't know the difference between good and evil any more? You should take all these things away from him! You should take the clothes off him and put him back out in the rain again! Germans like that deserve nothing, nothing!"

But the boy of whom she spoke paid no heed either to the woman, with her aging, fanatical face, or to the soldier, for he was spinning, with his arms outstretched, before the figure of the flushed, blond child who spun, in his bright new clothes, within the glass.

"Well, at home," said the soldier, and his voice was quiet as he counted the bills of military currency out; "at home, ma'am, I never had much occasion to do for other people, so I was glad to have had this opportunity offered me," he said, and then he went away.

The Lovers of Gain

The days in Germany were like the days in no other country, there to be breathed into being as one might breathe into the lips and nostrils of the dead. The hours of them seemed suspended, perhaps brought to a halt by the monumental rubble, but halted so long ago that it could no longer be recalled in what month, or year, or even in what lifetime, their sequence had reached this pause. Perhaps the bleak Teutonic twilight had set in as the reverberations of the final bomb faded to silence in the ruins, thought Mrs. Furley as she walked through the American Commissary door. Perhaps the meaning of night and day, of summer and winter, of peace and war, had been lost to this country in the instant when the last hope of German victory had died.

But once you stepped from the German city street, and into the Commissary, here, for better or worse, was the look of home. Metal push-wagons waited in a double row in the overheated entranceway, as they waited in the chain stores of any Stateside city you might name. Mrs. Furley showed her identification to the German girl seated at the desk, and picked up a meat number, and then she moved on with the others, as she had day after day of the year that had just elapsed—moved on with the young women in their saddleback shoes and bobby socks, pushing her wagon as they pushed theirs before them, moved into the thick of it with the matrons, the teen-age girls, the displaced grandmothers, some of them newly come from the States, who clung to the handles of their vehicles as if to the last remaining vestiges of a civilization they had always known. Scattered among them moved the men in uniform, the corporals, the staff sergeants, the lieutenants, the captains, the majors and colonels even, pushing their wagons as carefully as if babies rode in them, while they studied the lists their wives had written out.

On the shelves which lined and bisected the vast low hall were stacked the familiar cans and bottles—the names of Campbell, and Heinz, and Van Camp, and Fould, and Kellogg, to reassure the exiled, and beans and pancakes illustrated in color so that the fears of the lost and the bewildered might be allayed. But here the likeness to home came to an end, for nothing else was quite the same. Behind the vegetable counter, as behind the illuminated cases of meat, there were Germans, some lean and bespectacled and professorial, their natural habitat a laboratory or a lecture hall; and others solid and blond and canny-eyed, and still others as delicate-featured and long-haired as poets, all wearing the long, white chain-store dress. And the voice was German which pronounced the meat numbers slowly, painfully, through the microphone, saying: "Dirty, dirty, blease." Having drawn number sixty-one, Mrs. Furley pushed her wagon toward the corner where oranges and apples, and potatoes and cabbages, lay in refrigerated bins, their paucity enhanced by mirrors set above them along the walls. And here, one slender German poet came to life at Mrs. Furley's approach. She saw him slipping quickly through the other white-robed salesmen, maneuvering himself into position until only the bare wood of the counter lay between him and the American woman who had lived in Paris too.

"*Bon jour, madame,*" he would say in a low voice to her, as he stood putting his dark hair back with his black-rimmed fingers, a shy and tender look of yearning come into his eyes. "*Je suis* contented," he would say. He was no older than twenty-three or twenty-four, but, dressed up as a soldier in the Wehrmacht, he had occupied Paris with the others, and he liked to speak of the parks, and the avenues, and the monuments of a city that was never his, his voice lingering on the music of their names. "*Champs-Elysées, Champ-de-Mars, l'Arc de Triomphe,*" was one of the lines of poetry he recited to Mrs. Furley through the summer as he weighed the melons and tomatoes from Italy; or "*Place du Panthéon, Place de la Concorde, Boulevard Saint-Michel,*" he would say as he weighed the celery from New Jersey or the endives from Holland in the winter. But this time he said: "You did not come for one week. *Vous n'êtes pas venoo pour une semaine.*"

"Dirty-von, dirty-doo, dirty-tree, blease," said the voice from the meat counter, speaking through the microphone.

"Because I went to Paris for a week," said Mrs. Furley, and his eyes went dark with wonder in his eager face. (Once he had said to her that there were things which had disappointed him in Paris. The *Métros* were not kept clean, for instance, not as clean as the *S-bahn* in Berlin had been, he said. And he had spoken of the Paris pigeons, whose droppings defaced the statues in the public gardens, and the elegant façades. "Perhaps the Americans could tell the French to keep things cleaner," he had tried saying to her, smiling shyly.) "I brought you some cigarettes from Paris," she said to him now, and, as he passed the five-pound paper sack of Idaho potatoes across the counter to her, she put the packet of *Bleues* into his hand.

Or there was the one she had come to call Philip Morris, because that was the brand of cigarette he preferred. He had been three years a P.W. in England, and now his work was to roll the three-tiered carriers of bottled Danish milk in, rattling and clanking from the stockroom, and, as fast as the refrigerating-unit shelves were emptied, he would stack them full again. He was a man of fifty, or more, Philip Morris, with a wearily lidded eye, and hair turning gray, and he had a distinguished, high-bridged nose. His jowls were always cleanly shaven, the English he spoke was public school, and it would have seemed more fitting had he stood at the head of an operating table instead of trundling the milk carriers in in his long white surgeon's gown. He had spoken first of his insurance policy to Mrs. Furley, citing clauses which had been inserted, he said, in flagrant defiance of Occupation directives. He had even suggested that the matter be brought to the attention of Decartelization Branch, for the Germans, certain Germans, would be up to anything, he inferred, once the backs of the democratic and the just were turned. And another time he had spoken of Nietzsche to her, and once in a while of Schopenhauer; and on this occasion he opened the door of the refrigerating unit, as if drawing back a chair at a dinner table so that she might take her place among the enlightened who were already seated, and he spoke Plato's name.

"You will recall Plato's assertion that there are three classes of men," he said, and he selected the milk bottles for her from among those standing, long-necked and iced, upon the slatted shelves. "He defined them as the lovers of wisdom, the lovers of honor, and the lovers of gain," he said, as he set the bottles carefully in her wagon, side by side with the Super Suds, and the Crisco, and the Rowntree cocoa cans. "The lovers of wisdom," he said, his weary but masterful eyes on Mrs. Furley, "have been forgotten. They have not been called to the council tables, but are serving in menial positions in every fallen state. I study the faces of the men and the women who come through these doors, and it is not difficult to classify them. The lovers of wisdom are rarely observed among them," he said, and he closed the refrigerator door.

"And what of the lovers of honor?" said Mrs. Furley, and the voice at the microphone said, "Fourteen-sex, fourteen-seben, fourteen-ocht," while the bobby-socks wives, and the soldiers, and the grandmothers, moved forward in formation, pushing their burdened wagons as they came. "There are lovers of honor among them," Mrs. Furley said.

"Plato referred to the warriors when he spoke of the lovers of honor," explained the man called Philip Morris. "But the warriors are no longer the lovers of honor," he said, and he fixed the soldiers now with his cynic's gray eye. "The warriors are dead. They died in two world wars. Those who remain are the barterers. They know the price of coffee and cocoa and sugar and flour in a defeated country"; and, beyond him, the corporals and sergeants, the captains and majors, oblivious to the classification they had been given, moved, one behind the other toward the frozen meat, the lists their wives had written out for them held submissively in their hands.

"Won't you have a Philip Morris?" said Mrs. Furley, as she had said it week in and week out to him in the twelve months that had passed. And, although he seemed to have no great interest in it, he selected first one cigarette, and then a second, from the pack she held out to him; and he placed them with care in the monogrammed, silver case which he carried, with his pince-nez, in the pocket of his long, white, surgeon's gown.

The numbers fifty-two-and-three-and-four were called aloud now, and Mrs. Furley wheeled her wagon toward the shelves of Jack Frost sugars, and Crosse and Blackwell jams. And there a little woman with loose, white, flying hair, and a ravaged face, swept quickly, belligerently, with a broom made in Missouri, at the Commissary boards. The first thing she said was that she needed help, saying it in German under her breath to Mrs. Furley, but the plea already soured in her mouth, knowing there was no way for help to come.

"It's my husband. They put him in jail last night," she said, the tongue wagging, the broom sweeping, and the wild eye after it in pursuit while the tatters and remnants of the story fluttered on the air. "They oughtn't to lay their hands on him, the German police, as long as he's working for the *Amis*, but they picked him right up off the street and put him in jail!" She had been a beer-hall singer, a cabaret artist, she had once told Mrs. Furley; in the early twenties, she had danced the can-can for beer-hall drinkers in Berlin. "Maybe if an *Ami* went and spoke to the German police, they'd let him out," she said, not looking at Mrs. Furley, while the broom swept savagely across the boards. "He was walking along the street last night, and there, *Herr Gott,* was a man he hadn't seen in six long years, a man he wouldn't forget in all his life, and my husband went right up to him, and he got hold of him by the throat, and he started squeezing the life right out of him, the way he'd wanted to do for six long years, started shaking and squeezing him, and calling him the only names he deserved!" Her own throat seemed to choke now, for she could no longer find the breath to speak, and her fingers closed so tightly on the handle of the broom that the bones showed sharp enough to split the skin. "So the crowd that collected around them got hold of the police," she said when she could speak again, and the broom from Missouri swept wildly, crazily away. "And instead of letting my husband finish the man off, the police began beating my husband up, and then they dragged him off to jail! So he'll get the prison term, not the other one he's been seeing for six long years in his nightmares every night!" she said.

"But the man—the man he got by the throat—what had he done?" Mrs. Furley asked, and it did not matter if the numbers that were called through the microphone were nearing sixty now.

"So what had he done?" the little woman cried harshly out, and, as she whirled in her fury, the broom swept heedlessly across the feet of the lovers of honor or the lovers of gain who were passing, pushing their burdened carts. "So what had he done?" she cried out, her ire rising at the sight of them, for here was a torment, more profound than hunger, which no illicit coffee or cocoa or sugar, and no brand of foreign tobacco could assuage. "My husband's mother and sister, it was going to be all right for them," she said, her lips drawn back in a grimace from the bad taste in her mouth. "It was fixed up for them to get away. They were going to get to Geneva.

That was in 1943. But they were denounced, denounced, denounced!" she cried out in a low voice, not speaking to anyone at all. "That's what that man did, he denounced them. That's all he did, denounced them," she said, and, beneath the hem of the chain-store dress, her legs had the liveliness and spring still of a dancer's legs who had danced the can-can for beer-hall drinkers in Berlin. "Perhaps if an *Ami* spoke to the police," she said, and then she seemed suddenly to recognize the folly of calling as witness the humble dead. "You're always looking for Hellman's mayonnaise," she said, sweeping on past the angel-food and gingerbread mixes, past Aunt Jemima's smiling face. "They got some in this morning, over there with the bottled sauces," she said.

Mrs. Furley reached the meat counter as the man at the microphone said, "Zickstee." He was seated hunched on a high, leather-cushioned stool, with his legs drawn up beneath the white skirt of his dress. He was a small man, and his lips were full and ruby red, and his nose was flamboyantly nostrilled, and a nest of tight, black, oily curls clung to the back of his skull. There were curls as well in his outsized ears, and his eyeballs were swollen, as if from a lifetime of falling, burning tears, and the whites of them were bound by scarlet veins. He was singular in that the names of Chesterfield, or Pall Mall, or Camel, could not be given him, as they could be given the others, for he had no interest in any brand of cigarette, as if by this one gesture of repudiation he cleared himself, and every member of his race, of the charge of barter and venality.

"Zo, hallo," he greeted Mrs. Furley when she paused by the microphone to surrender her number to him, and then he went on talking of the theatre to her, for the moment not calling the meat numbers aloud. Before the war, before Hitler's time, he had always worked in the theatre, he had told her from the beginning, but it was never made clear in what capacity he served. "I like the vork in the theatre better as vorking here," he would say, with a curved and painful grin stretching his mouth. "I begin vorking in the theatre in London. I learn to zpick the langvich there. That vas ober tventy years ago," he would say. And once he had said: "I vork for an American in London, a director-producer, a Jew from New York, but a nize Jew," sitting there hunched in his white dress on the stool, smiling his anguished smile at Mrs. Furley.

"Why do you say 'a nice Jew'?" asked Mrs. Furley. "What happened to you that you have to speak like this?"

But the answer had already been given in the history of the country, and nothing that had been said since had been said with power or passion enough to take that answer away. In concentration camp, and out of it, he had heard the radio voices and the other voices naming the outcast, heard them year after year, and over and over, describing the anatomy of evil until he had come to recognize in shame the stigma of his own reflection in the glass.

"Vell, zome Jews nize, zome not zo nize, that's vat they tell me," he had said, still smiling at her, and he had shrugged aside the responsibility for any of it. "Zo, hallo," he said to her now. "You vent to the theatre in Paris?"

"I saw a play called 'La Soif,' " said Mrs. Furley. "A play by Bernstein called 'Thirst.' "

"Oh, 'Zirst,' " said the little man on the stool. " 'Zirst,' " he repeated in sudden bewilderment, and the sound of the word was whispered strangely through the microphone, as the voice of an entire people might have whispered it from a vast, still-open grave, before those lying in it had expired.

Mrs. Furley walked in past the illuminated cases where slices of beef liver, gray with frost, and suitable as tiling with which to roof a house, were spread on platters on display. The hamburger must be chiselled away in icy formations, she knew, and the brook trout pried from the granite block into which their once supple bodies had been frozen fast.

"I think I'll have a leg of mutton today," said Mrs. Furley, and the butcher she had named Lucky Strike peered through his thick-lensed glasses at her, as if studying the angles of a parallelogram.

"How many?" he asked, as he had asked it week after week across the shining counter, with a cook's white cap set gravely on his head.

"Well, I think one will be enough this time," said Mrs. Furley, as she had said it, with patience, all year to him, for it was perhaps the purest logic to believe that, dead or living, a mutton had four legs. "Won't you have a Lucky?" she added, and the German called Lucky Strike brought the pack of them slowly into focus behind his lenses, and then reached out his hand.

The Lost

T HE WAR had scarcely come to a close when an American Relief Team drove up in jeeps through the little hills of Bavaria toward a property which had been, in former times, a baronial farmer's demesne. The place was set back off the country road, a good ten kilometers from any village, and the tree-bordered lane which led to the vast manor house, and its barns and stables and dependent buildings, had long since become a cattle-and-wagon road, deeply rutted in the mud of springtime, and encumbered with stones. The heavy iron gates hung, as derelict as unhinged shutters, from the scarred blocks of granite which had stood for generations at the entrance to the drive. There were wild birds flickering through the branches of the trees, but no other sign of life; and even before

173

the Americans had mounted the cathedral-like steps, and opened the massive door of the stone-winged house, they felt the chill of winter and silence and death that stood like a presence in its feudal halls.

The place had served as a Selection Camp from 1938 to 1945, so that any vestiges of personal effects or of individual life had been eradicated a long time before. But the official records of those who had passed through it, on their way to forced labor or to extermination, were found, neatly and alphabetically filed, in the bookshelves of what had once been the ancestral library. Attached to these records were the photographs, each with a number stencilled across the base of it, and each reproducing the grief and the exhaustion of one human being's unforgettable face—photographs of men with rumpled shirt collars and ties either missing or askew, taken full face as well as in profile, in order that the full measure of their anguish might be known; and photographs of women, some wearing blouses caught by antique brooches at their necks, and others in variously patterned aprons, as if they had come from their kitchens or their housework to this place, without having had the time to do their hair. It was the eyes of these men and women, who were there no longer, which looked now at the Americans, and beyond them, upon some indescribable vista of hopelessness and pain.

But when the Americans came, the nature of the place was altered. It became a Children's Center, and children who had journeyed from factory to factory throughout the war, or drifted from home to temporary home, were brought here from wherever they were found, brought singly, or in couples, or in groups. If they had wandered so long that they could no longer remember their people's names, new names were given them, and they were given Displaced Persons' cards, these children from Poland, or Holland, or Czecho-Slovakia, or Hungary. They were known as Unaccompanied Children, and they were given clothes to wear, and food to eat, and the outline of a plausible future at last. The Americans set up slides and swings on the grass of the lawn that lay between the stables and the manor house, and they made a sandpile for them, and then began the long and painful probing of their memories.

It was these slides and swings which the three boys saw first when they rode up on the American Army truck one morning —the wooden slides with the dew of the spring night still beading them, and the empty swings swaying gently on their ropes in the clear morning air. The soldier at the wheel brought the truck to a halt at the curve of the drive, and the three boys who had ridden in front with him waited a moment, looking out through the window and the windshield, reluctant, it seemed, to leave the Army vehicle and commit themselves to a civilian site and setting, for this was a part of life of which they knew nothing at all. Then the boy sitting next to the door pushed it open and jumped down—a tall, dark-haired boy of fifteen or sixteen maybe—and the other two followed, jumping clear of the step and down onto the gravel drive.

The tall one wore a faded khaki battle jacket, with the length of the sleeves turned back in cuffs, and a strip of German parachute silk, mottled green and tan, and as soft as the wings of a moth, knotted around his long curved neck. The jacket was buckled in tight where the waist of a man was intended to be, but the boy had no hips to hold it up, so it hung down long on the shabby G.I. trousers which had been cut down to his size. The two other boys were younger; they were twelve or fourteen, maybe, but they too were dressed like deserters from the ranks of the same army. They wore khaki, machine-made sweaters over their G.I. shirts, and their khaki trousers were thrust inside the mud-caked boots of the U.S. Infantry.

"Thanks for the lift," said the tall boy, speaking as good American as you might hear at home. He stood looking up with a kind of deference at the soldier sitting behind the wheel of the truck, and the soldier looked down at the three of them, and fumbled a package of chewing gum out of one pocket of his khaki pants.

"You guys like a stick of gum?" he said, and each of them reached casually up, and took a stick from the package he held.

And then the soldier slammed the truck door closed, and he started the motor, and the three boys stood there, chewing fiercely, the bits of tin foil and the colored paper lying on the driveway under their feet, as they watched the truck back up and go. They had met for the first time the night before, and even when the truck was gone, they did not look into one another's faces for any of the answers that might be given, each in his own fashion seeking to dissemble his timidity. The tall one, his shoulders slouched in the battle jacket, put his hands into his trouser pockets, and his dark, grave eyes looked across the lawn toward the slides and the swings, and the thickly leafed branches of the trees. The boy who was second in size had a square, tawny-colored face, with a short nose and a humorous mouth, and he stooped at once and picked up a pebble from the driveway, and sent it skimming toward the sandpile where it hit hard against the side of a child's wooden bucket that had been forgotten in the dark, damp sand. The youngest boy's hair was of the texture and color of a pony's shaggy, chestnut hide, his skin was delicate and white, and he had a shy, quiet look of expectancy, of hope even, in his wide, auburn eyes.

"I bet a nickel that's the kitchen over there," he said in a high, bright voice, and he jerked his chin toward the right wing of the house.

"You hurtin' for chow already?" said the second boy. His accent might have come straight from Brooklyn, except that it had come from somewhere else before that, and, as he spoke, he folded his arms upon his breast, and spat casually across the drive.

The tall boy looked back from the trembling leaves in the strong, ancient branches, his eyes sober, his head hanging heavy on his soiled slender neck.

"Let's go on up and sign ourselves in," he said, the drawl of of his voice having come, it seemed, from a Southern state. "That's what we come here for," he said.

He led the way up the worn stone steps, and through the panelled door that stood open, having summoned courage, now that there was no other choice before them, to face this that was not an army deal. The youngest boy, his back and shoulders straight, and his hands in his trouser pockets, followed behind him, but the second boy lingered on the driveway, skimming stones across the grass. Because it was early still, there was no murmur of life in the house, and after they had come into the flagstoned hall, the tall boy moved on tiptoe toward the flight of stairs. But, at the foot of it, he stopped, and he jerked the battle jacket he wore up to where his waist should be, and tried to peg it on his hipbones. Then he lifted his thin, big-knuckled hands, and he smoothed back his lank black locks of hair.

"Hey, I smell chow," the other boy whispered behind him, but he did as the tall boy did, and sat down upon the first step of the stairs.

"Where'd you pick up you' outfit?" the tall boy asked, speaking quietly.

"Anzio," said the youngest boy, looking up into his face. "My mom and dad, they was bumped off when we bombed the town. I join up with the Fourth Rangers and done the whole campaign with them," he said.

"My buddy's a mechanic, he's an ignition expert. I been suhvicing cars with him since 1944," said the tall boy, the words spoken soft and low. "He done tried every way there was to take me back, but they just couldn't see it," he said. He was leaning forward, his elbows on his knees, his long hands dangling. "We wanted to do it legitimate. When they Z.I.'d him last week, he told me to come straight off down here and see what they could do."

And now the second boy came slowly up the outside steps, and crossed the threshold in hostility, wanting none of what might be offered here.

"Why the hell don't we make a break and run for it?" he said, stopping before the two others on the stairs. He stood there, recalcitrant, resentful, the lids narrowed on his opaque, black eyes, speaking savagely to them through his teeth. "You guys too yellow?" he said.

"Breakin' out won't get us nowhere," said the tall boy quietly.

"It'll get us the hell out of this here kid joint," said the second one. He fumbled a half-empty pack of Lucky Strikes from his trouser pockets, and put a cigarette on his lip. "Christ knows I didn't ask to come here," his Brooklyn accent said.

178

"None of us done asked," said the tall boy, and the smallest boy raised his head, and looked toward the end of the hallway.

"I bet a nickel it's ham and eggs," he said.

Because he was standing facing the stairs, it was the second boy who saw her first. It was only when the hot sullenness in his eyes had shifted to alarm, and, with the cigarette on his lip still, he had spoken the words of blasphemy under his breath, and turned, and gone out the door again, that the two others knew someone was there. She was big, and gray-haired, and matronly, and she held a flowered cotton dressing gown around her as she looked down from the landing at them through the steel-rimmed spectacles that rode her nose.

"Hello," she said. The two boys had got to their feet, and they stood looking up at her.

"Hello," the tall one and the small one said.

"You men come up to the bathroom and wash your hands," the gray-haired woman said to them. "I'll get some clothes on, and then we'll have breakfast with the rest"; and it might have been mother or aunt, who was saying these things to them, except that neither mother nor aunt, nor the prototype of these, had meaning for them. It was not these names, these words in any tongue, that could stir the memory of anything they knew.

"Maybe you been expecting us, ma'am," the tall boy said.

"We're G.I. mascots from Bremerhaven," said the small boy, saying it with pride.

"You bet," the woman said. She did not say "so you're two more the M.P.s got when you were trying to slip onto the transport," although it may have come into her head. She did not put any of the questions to them until breakfast had been eaten, with the hundred-odd others, at the long tables in the dining hall. Then she took them away, a hand laid on each shoulder, into a room that was furnished with wicker armchairs, with flowered chintz cushions tied in the seats, and she took her place behind a paper-encumbered desk, and she looked at the two boys through the steel-rimmed spectacles on her nose. "Sit down, men," she said, and she watched them sit down on the cushions of the wicker chairs. "If it's easier for you to speak German, we can talk German together," she said.

"I been speaking American three-year now," said the tall boy. "I learn German working in a munition factory. I done near forget every word of it I knew."

"And before that?" asked the woman, but she still did not write anything down.

"Czech," the tall boy said.

The woman did not seem to hear his answer, for she went on speaking of other things, as if saying these things to herself, speaking of countries and peoples the boys had perhaps known once but which they scarcely remembered, and in whose present and future they no longer had a part.

"It's like a big puzzle, or like the pieces of a big vase somebody dropped and broke here, right on the ground in Europe," she was saying, "and the pieces are jumbled together, and maybe we'll never get it straight, because a lot of the pieces are lost. We're trying to find them and put them together. That's what we're trying to do here, and we're doing it slowly, and maybe we're not even doing it very well," she said, and the sunlight from the window glinted on her glasses as she talked. "Maybe the G.I.s you were with made you promises about going to the States," she went on saying, and the two boys sitting in the wicker armchairs seemed to come alive now as they listened to her, but to the tall boy at least she was neither woman nor American, perhaps not human being even, but a voice—disembodied, quiet, direct—which might be coming now to the words they had been waiting to hear her say. "And probably when the G.I.s made you those promises they thought they would be able to keep them," she said. "I've talked to some of these men, I've had letters from them, and I know they believed they would be able to keep the promises. But there were other kinds too. There were some kinds who didn't care what happened to you men afterward. I've known that kind too. They wanted you to learn how to drink and smoke and gamble and shoot crap and use the kind of language they used—"

"I begin shooting crap in Naples," the small boy said in his high, eager voice. "I clean up seven bucks the first night there."

"Look, kid," the woman said abruptly, "if Italy's your country, perhaps you ought to pack up and go back there. You think it over. Perhaps that's where it's right for you to be."

He was sitting upright on the edge of the wicker chair, the khaki shirt open at his neck, the shaggy pony's chestnut hair growing long at his temples and behind his ears, the cut-down G.I. trousers bagging at his knees. He faced the woman for one more untroubled instant, and then the brightness perished in his flesh, and he looked down in grief at the mud-caked boots of the U.S. Infantry.

"I ain't no Eyetie no more," he said, and he did not raise his eyes to look at her because of the tears that were standing in them. "I'm American. I wanna go home where my outfit's gone," he said.

"Wait," said the woman quietly. "What would happen to you over there? We're an organization, and we make our list of candidates for emigration, and then the American Consul decides. We got thirty-five over last year, sent to adoption centers. But there's one thing we can't do much about changing —if you have anyone left to go back to in your own country, then we've agreed we'll send all you men back," she said.

"But if you ain't got nobody left where you come from?" the tall boy said, leaning forward from his chair.

"How do you know you haven't anyone left?" said the woman.

"My folks was hung in Noverzcimki in '42, when the Germans come in," he said.

"What proof have you got of that?" asked the woman.

"I done saw it," the tall boy said, and as the sunlight struck the woman's glasses, she swiftly lifted her hand, as if warding off a blow.

It was after that that she took out the forms and arranged them on the table, holding the fountain pen in readiness above them as she spoke.

"Tell me your name," she said to the tall boy, not looking at his face.

"Janos—it used to be Janos when I was a kid," he said. "But in the army they called me Johnny Madden." He leaned a little further forward, his thin shoulders hunched, his dark, anxious eyes fixed on her. "He wrote you a letter about me. He wrote it last week. Did you get it yet?" he said.

"Yes—a letter. I got a letter from a man named Madden," said the woman, her fountain pen still moving across the paper. "He's on his way back to Chattanooga. He's got a partnership in a garage."

"Partnership with his brother-in-law," the tall boy said, shifting further forward in his intensity. "Sergeant Charlie

Madden. He want me to try to get over legitimate. That's why he tole me to come down here."

"Yes," said the woman again. She stopped writing now, and her middle-aged hands straightened the papers on her desk. "He's colored, isn't he?" she said, and now the gray eyes, that might have been aunt's or mother's eyes behind the spectacles, lost their anonymity, and they looked at him in inexpressible kindliness.

"That's right," said the tall boy. "His wife, she done pass on back in '43, and he ain't got no one left to care for. He's an ignition expert, and I learn how to suhvice cars with him. He's got fifteen hundred dollars put in the bank, so he's able to pay for me to come."

"Yes," said the woman. "He wrote me that." She sat there silent, musing a moment, while the tall boy leaned forward from the chair, his eyes asking the question of her even before the words were spoken out.

"Do you think I got a chance of getting over there, ma'am?" he said.

"We can only recommend," the woman said quietly at last. "We don't have any final say." When she was done with the forms, she told them that they could go; they could go to the foreman in the workshop and find out what there was to do, and in the afternoon they would be processed by the Supply and Medical Corps. "You'll get on to the ropes," she said, and they stood before her, the tall one and the short one, incongruously matched. "The third man who came with you, the one who went out to take a walk," she said, "you tell him he needs a license to go fishing. That's what most of them start in doing when they're uneasy here. And he didn't get any breakfast. Tell him we mess at twelve o'clock," she said.

But all day the others did not see the third boy. Wherever he was, he did not come in at the sound of the mess-hall bell at noontime, and he was not in the empty classrooms or in the workshops, or the dormitories, and he was not outside with the children who played underneath the trees. The boy from An-zio swung on the bars with the others in the afternoon, and had the third boy been there, he could have been seen at a glance, for he would have stood out as a stranger among them, perhaps lingering, handsome and sullen and contemptuous, on the out-skirts of their activity. Janos went seeking him through the buildings, through the barns and stables, and down the fields that lay behind the house. As he walked, he unknotted the para-chute silk from around his neck in the heat, and he fanned it at the thin young wasps which swam about his head. In the gully below, where it seemed to him that water must pass, he could see an area of pine trees stretched in an isthmus of shadow in the pale, shining sea of grass and flowering bush. And there, at the end of the path, where the fast full stream poured musically from the trees, he found the third boy sit-ting, his back in the khaki shirt turned against the fields and against the house, as if against the sight and sound of all hu-manity.

"If you just goes up there and tells her your name and every-thing, then you got a chance," Janos said to him at once. "You got the same chance as Anzio and me." The boy was sitting on the bank, with the khaki sweater pulled off and lying beside the cast-off combat boots on the freshly trampled grass. He had rolled the legs of his G.I. trousers up, and his strong bare legs were hanging in the stream. "She fills out the papers that you got to have, and if they finds out for sure that you got no-body of you' folks left back where you come from, then you has a chance," said Janos. He stood, tall and stoop-shouldered, beside the other boy, watching the water flow swiftly over his naked feet, and mount high upon his muscular brown calves.

"Nuts," said the Brooklyn accent on this alien air, and the boy moved one foot slowly back and forth in the running water of the stream. The side of his face looked golden in the sunlight, and the dark hair lay thick and glossily dressed upon his shapely head. "I got the whole thing lined up. Have a butt," he said, and he took the crumpled paper of Lucky Strikes from his pocket, and held it out toward Janos. "I been looking around. It couldn't be sweeter," the boy said. Janos took a cigarette from the boy's hand, and he straightened it carefully in his fingers. Then the boy brought a silver lighter out of his pocket, and flicked it with his thumb, and Janos leaned to light his cigarette at the puny flame which the boy held shielded in the cup of his smooth hand. "I been contacting people in the area. Natives," the boy said, and he lit his own cigarette. As he drew the first breath of it in, he snapped the lighter closed again. "I got a deal on if you wanta come in on it. I got it fixed up with a Kraut down the road," he said.

"What kind of a deal?" asked Janos.

And now he sat down on the grass of the stream bank, folding his long legs awkwardly, as a young horse will, and settling down in the shimmering tide of sun.

"I'm going over the hill tonight," said the other boy. "All the good guys that come here, they don't stay. I got that straight from the Krauts," he said. He leaned back on his elbows, his eyes half closed against the smoke of the cigarette hanging on his lip. "All this here kid stuff. Don't let them give you the run-around," he said. "Swings, slides, sandpiles, and standing in line for a bowl of Grape Nuts. I'm through with that kind of crap. I'm fourteen. I got tired of hanging my stocking up for Christmas about ten years ago."

"You going back where you come from?" Janos said.

He sat smoking the cigarette, his shoulders hunched, his long legs drawn up, and his thin arms clasped around them, looking away across the flowing stream.

"Do I look like a dope?" the other boy said, and he gave a jerk of laughter. "I come from Poland once, but that don't mean I'm going back there. I been two and a half years with the Army, and I got my campaign ribbons, and my overseas service stripes, and I know my way around this little continent." The smoke from his mouth drifted lazily across the sun-lit air, and his feet hung in the clear cool water still. "I'm going where things is easier. I'm going where all my friends is doing business now," he said.

"The sergeant I was with," Janos began saying after a moment, "he come from Tennessee. We been working together since '44. When I get over there, I can start right in working with him again."

"Sure. You bet," said the other boy in irony.

"So I'll stick around here until the papers comes through," said Janos.

"You must be kidding, bud," the other boy said. "I saw action with three different outfits," he said then, and the sound of derision was gone from his voice as he turned his mutinous eyes on Janos's face. "I done everything that every son-of-a-bitch in the army ever done. I done peter parade, and had my broads, and wrote my own Saturday-night passes out, and, sure, they was all going to take me home with them, the whole God-damn Army was going to see to it poissonnaly that I got Z.I.'d when the rest of them was! Sure, all you had to do was go to Bremerhaven when they went, and walk up the gang-plank with them, and nobody'd ever stop you, nobody'd ever have a word to say. Nobody except the M.P.s, the God-damn bastards," he said, and he lay there, looking back at the water again, and calling them the several names. "I got three times to Bremerhaven," he went on saying after that, "but I didn't get no further. The first time it was the colonel who had the uniform issued me in '44 who was going to see that I got shipped back when the others went. Except he forgot to fix the M.P.s, just a little detail like that he forgot!" he said in high, fierce irony. "Sure, they'll wave to you from the deck when the troop ship pulls out, and when they get home they'll send you a postcard of the Statue of Liberty! Up in Bremerhaven, they'll tell you just how it can be done, and the brass hats gives you advice for free. Run along to one of these God-damn kid centers, where they'll fix your immigration papers up! Hell, I ain't asking no favors of nobody! I been two and a half years in the American Army. I'm no emigrant," he said, and he shot the butt of his cigarette away.

Janos sat smoking a little while in silence, watching the water stream quickly, melodiously, past.

"That sergeant I was talking about, Sergeant Charlie Madden," he said after another moment, "he used to tell me a lot of things. He used to tell me how they first started measuring the days and nights," he said.

"You can't measure days and nights," said the other boy, but now the scorn was gone, and his voice seemed inexplicably filled with sorrow.

"Sure; way back in the time of emperors, they started in measuring the days and nights," said Janos. "They started in measuring them by letting water fall. They done took two

187

jars, and when the sun come up in the morning, they let the water start dripping from one jar into the other, and when the last drop fell, the sun was already setting, and that was the end of the day. And to measure the nights, they let the water drip back into the jar it come from first," he went on saying, his legs drawn up and clasped in his arms still, his sober eyes looking at the trees. "And the drops of the water falling for a thousand years was like the ticking of a clock. Charlie Madden said for a thousand years they measured up the nights and days that way."

"Christ, I need a drink," said the other boy, and he sat up abruptly. "Listen, kid, if I let you in on this deal, we could make a break together," he said. He took his feet out of the stream, and he spread his toes in the warmth of the sun, and the beads of water ran off his smooth brown legs and feet and glistened on the grass. "This Kraut down the road, he's doing business with the Army—a nice little racket in jewels and schnapps. There're a lot of big shots in the country around here, and they don't want to contact the Army direct, so this Kraut, he picks up their family jewels and their cases of schnapps, and he does it for them. The Army truck, it comes down from Frankfurt at night, maybe two-three times in the week it comes, with a load of coffee and cocoa they lifted out of the commissary depot stock."

Janos drew in the last deep breath of smoke from his cigarette, and then he threw the end of it away, and his long fingers reached out and pulled at a stalk of grass which grew tall beside the stream.

"And then what are you aiming to do?" he said, and he put the fresh, bleached end of the blade of grass between his teeth.

"I'm going to hop that Army truck back to Frankfurt,

188

maybe tonight, maybe tomorrow night. The Kraut down the road's fixing it up for me," the other boy said.

"And what'll you do once you git to Frankfurt?" asked Janos, chewing slowly at the end of grass.

"The truck drops you off at Rhine-Main," the other boy said quickly. "By that time it's maybe three-four in the morning, and the M.P.s is groggy, and you slip in when they're loading the 'transat' plane. The next stop's Gander, and then New Yoik." He smiled with one side of his humorous mouth at Janos. "Do you get it?" he said.

That night was the first night Janos wrote to Charlie Madden. He wrote him to his home address in Chattanooga, sitting there in the chintz-bedecked, lamplit room where the gray-haired woman had put the questions to them in the day. She had drawn up a wicker chair on the other side of the table from him now, and the lamplight fell on the paper she had given him, and on the knitting in her hands, as she helped him with the words he couldn't spell.

"I just wanted to let Charlie Madden know what the score is," Janos said when he had written the first lines out, and he waited, as if there were some answer to be given.

"Nobody knows the score," said the woman, knitting. "It's like life," she said, as mother or aunt might have said it to him. "You have to wait and see." Mother or aunt, she thought as she knitted, knowing the look of her own face in the glass; knowing it was neither mother nor aunt that any of them wanted, but the other things they had learned how to pronounce the names of—the name of a game of cards, or of a regiment whose insignia they had worn two years now, or the name of a city they had never known; or else the smell of a special beverage, or even the smell of car grease, or the turning motor of an

Army car. "The other one, the one who went out for a walk this morning," she said, saying it casually, her needles knitting still.

"He's a little doubtful about coming inside and signing up," said Janos, speaking slowly, softly, his eyes fixed on the words he had written carefully out.

"Sometimes they'll stay out for a week, and then they'll come in," the woman said. "You tell him the food is good. You tell him we're not M.P.s." Or aunts or mothers either, she did not say, still knitting. "You tell him we leave you free."

"Yes, ma'am," said Janos, but it might have been he had not been listening to her. "Please, how does you spell 'ignition'?" he said.

But the other boy didn't leave on the truck that night, and he didn't go the next night. He had settled himself in the hay-loft above the empty stables, and only Janos knew that he was there. The second night he said he was getting a bottle of schnapps from the German farmer in exchange for two packs of cigarettes, and Janos said he would carry food out from the mess hall to him. So that was the way it began. All day the boy from Anzio played with the other children on the swings and slides, or else he worked in the classroom, or he went to the vegetable garden with the others and helped pull the radishes and the new lettuce out. He did not wear the cut-down G.I. clothes any more, but boy's short trousers, as the others did, and he did not speak of his outfit any longer. And Janos did what Charlie Madden had taught him to do in the shed behind the house where the driveway came to an end—all day he cleaned the carburetors, and checked the ignition, and over-hauled the motors, of the American Relief Team's cars. But

190

when it grew dark, he went out the back door with his head down, and he passed the shed with the cars standing in it, and he went on toward the stable underneath the trees. He wore his battle jacket still, for they did not have the other things to fit him, and inside his jacket he carried the bread and the cheese and whatever else he had slipped from the mess-hall tables after the evening meal was done. Once inside the stable door, he crossed in the darkness to the thick-runged ladder, and he felt with one hand for the polished wood, and closed his fingers on it, and then he began to climb.

But on the third night, the boy in the loft was still drinking water. For half a carton of cigarettes, he said, the farmer had given the bottle of schnapps to an American Army colonel instead of to him, and he lay cursing the farmer. But on the fourth night he had the bottle. He lay stretched in the farthest corner on the hay, with the square of a window standing open in the boards above him, and the stars shining clearly in it, and Janos could hear his voice speaking out across the hay-sweet dark.

"My God-damn lighter's gone dry as a witch's tit," the boy said, and Janos could hear the rasp of the lighter's stone in his hand. "I got to get me to a P.X. and get me some lighter fluid. I got to find me an American shoe-repair and get some soles put on my shoes. I walked through 'em today, but I got the schnapps," he said. When he sat up in the hay, his head and his neck and his shoulders in the G.I. sweater showed dark against the starry square of night. "Have a swig, kid," he said, and the bottle was more than half empty then when Janos drank from it. He had to tip his head far back, and hold the bottle tilted before the sharp hot trickle of liquid ran into his throat. "I got to get me to a man's-size town where there's a P.X. quick," the boy was saying in the darkness. "I bet I got two weeks' ration of butts coming due."

"Maybe when you hits Frankfurt," Janos said, and he wiped his mouth off, and stood the bottle up carefully in the hay, and now, without warning, the other boy began to laugh. He lay laughing beyond Janos in the darkness, shaking with laughter, as if something had come loose inside him, and was rattling around hard inside his belly and his chest.

"In that hick town?" he said, and he lay there swearing at the name of Frankfurt, and laughing in dry, hard jerks of sound.

"I got hole of a piece of sausage for you tonight," Janos said when the laughing had stopped a little. He had undone the buttons of his battle jacket, and now he laid the bread and the cheese and the sausage on the hay.

"For Christ's sake, pass me the bottle," the other boy said, and when Janos found it in the darkness, he passed it to the unseen, outstretched hand.

"My buddy, that sergeant I was telling you about, he could tell you the names of all the stars there is," he said, and he sat looking at the stars in the open, bluish square of night. "They might be one place in winter, and another place in the summertime," said Janos, "but he'd call them for you. We was in three countries together, and the same stars was usually there."

There was a lingering suck of air as the other boy lowered the bottle from his mouth.

"Oh, Christ," he said, his voice sounding thick and strange and far. "I'm thinking of the brass, the God-damn brass," he said. "I'm thinking how everything they got—chow, or cartons of butts, or pieces of hide—was always bigger and better than what we got." And then he began to laugh again, and he lay there, shaking as he jerked the laughter out. "Have a drink," he said, handing the bottle across the hay-whispering, hay-fragrant, dark.

Janos closed his fingers around the bottle's neck, and then he drank, and with the second long swallow of the liquor, the promise made was no longer a thing that lay, heavy with longing, in his blood. It had come alive now, and he no longer doubted as he handed the bottle back across the hay.

"I know if I just sticks around here, and works, and waits," he began saying, and then he stopped it to say something else. "He taught me how to write in the two years we been together. I wrote him every night since I been here," he said.

"You listen, kid," said the other boy after he had drunk again. "The cards is stacked against us. We ain't got a chance, not you and me. Frankfurt," he said, in the same far thick voice, "I'm through with Frankfurt. I heard the air strip at Rhine-Main wasn't so good, so I changed the plans I had. I go down to the Kraut's place this morning, and he tells me the M.P.s got the guys that was in the set-up with him, and they puts them in the clink. Bust up a nice little racket because they wasn't getting a big enough slice of it themselves. To hell with Frankfurt. I'm going to work a bigger area, like Munich, or Berlin," he said. He lifted the bottle of schnapps and drank again, and the stars stood sharper and brighter in the open window above his head. After a moment, he lowered the bottle from his mouth. "You got dependents anywheres?" he said.

"I ain't got nobody," said Janos. "That's why I know it's going to be all right, and I won't have to be going back home again."

"My old lady, she must've been fixing chow," the other boy

said, his voice muffled now, as if he were holding the laughter in. "Because when I come home from school, there was her arm sticking out the end where the kitchen used to be. A direct hit. Pretty neat for '41," he said. "I couldn't get over the gold bracelet that was hanging on her arm still. Funny as hell how the bracelet wasn't twisted or nothing—"

"Maybe gold don't twist," said Janos.

"Maybe it don't at that," the other boy said across the hay.

That was the last time Janos ever saw him. When he climbed the rungs of the ladder the next evening, the boy was gone, and there was only the empty bottle lying in the hay. But because nobody else had known that he was there, no one else knew that he had gone, and the children stood in line for meals, or swung on the swings, or filed into the classrooms, and even the official memory of him was lost in the endless shuffling of children, effaced by the endlessly changing faces and names and histories. Once the gray-haired woman had said to Janos: "That other one, the one who went out to take a walk, you tell him we're having fried chicken this evening," and then the sound of her voice had perished of itself, as if knowing it had come beyond this, and there was nothing left that any living woman might find to say.

Twice in the next month the repatriation trucks came in through the heavy iron gates, and the children left, twenty or thirty at a time, carrying their string-tied bundles in their hands. As the trucks moved off down the driveway, the children sang in high clear voices of hope, returning now to places and people they did not remember ever having seen; perhaps to people who had been mother or father once, and to countries called France, and Holland, and Poland, and Czecho-Slovakia, and Hungary. And after a while the boy from Anzio left too, and the afternoon he left, the woman of the American team came down to the shed and looked through her steel-rimmed spectacles at Janos working on the Army car.

"He had a grandfather in Naples," she said, and she sat down, in her rose-colored sweater and her old gray skirt, on an empty case marked "Tomato Juice" that stood against the side wall of the shed. "And that grandfather never stopped looking for him, he never stopped giving his name and his description to every G.I. he met." Janos was on his knees by the car, smearing the grease on the wheel nuts with his long thin hands. "And now he's on his way back," she said, "and he'll grow up in Italy where he belongs. I wish you were all as easy as that. Your papers, Janos," she said, and for a moment she did not say any more. She sat pressing the gray stuff of her skirt out under her square, strong palms, and she did not look at Janos. "They've checked back on the records, and the Consul says it's official enough that your people were killed. There's nobody of your family left," she said, but it did not seem easy for her to say.

Janos did not move at once; he crouched by the car a little longer, his shoulders hunched, scarcely daring to hear this thing that she had said. And then he undid himself slowly, the long legs straightening joint by joint, the long bent torso coming erect, until he stood up in the shadow of the shed, wiping the car grease from his hands.

"So I can write Charlie Madden it's all right about my coming over?" he said, and he felt his own mouth shaking as he smiled.

"Well, that's what I wanted to talk to you about," the woman said. She sat there below him on the upturned box, carefully and steadily smoothing the stuff of her gray skirt out. "Over

there, back home, in the States, it isn't the same as here about a
lot of things—"

"Why, sure, ma'am, I knows that," Janos said, and then the
fear closed on his heart again. "If I ain't got nobody left, then
I'm all right, ain't I?" he said. "If my folks was all killed off,
then I'm eligible to go?"

"Well, Charlie Madden," she said, beginning again, "he's
colored. Maybe in a combat outfit you didn't hear much talk
about men being colored or men being white, or maybe you
didn't pay much attention to it if you did. But over there, back
home, in the States, there's the color question."

"There's what?" said Janos.

"There's the color question," she said in a dogged, quiet
voice, and she did not lift her head to look at him. "There's the
question about people being colored or people being white,"
she said. "In some parts of the country at home, they don't live
in the same part of town that white people live. And they don't
always go to the same schools, or to the same doctors when
they're sick." Janos stood there listening to the words she said,
and, as he listened, the woman again ceased being woman,
ceased being human being even, and it was merely a voice in
the shed that spoke quietly and bitterly of the separate lives
that must be lived by people of different colors, as she had on
that first day spoken of the hopes that might never come to
anything at all. The voice was troubled as it searched logic or
history for justification of the nearly incredible story it told. "I
cannot explain to you why it is like this, but it *is* like this," it
said, the voice faltering in the telling. "So if you did get to the
States, there wouldn't be any way for you to live with Charlie
Madden. The Consul's office has talked it over with me, and
we thought we'd put it up to you. If we put your name on our

list, and if you were cleared for emigration, then it would be better if you went to another family, a white family. We'd explain to them about Charlie Madden, and all he'd done for you over here," she said, "and he could come and see you, and you'd still be able to be friends—" and then the voice came to an end, and there was silence in the shed. The gray-haired, bespectacled woman sat on the wooden box against the wall and looked down at the backs of her hands, and the boy in his khaki clothes stood motionless between her and the dismantled car, seeming not even to breathe.

"I got all Charlie Madden's letters," he said then. "He don't make no mention of anything like that at all."

"The adoption committee might find somebody for you who had a garage himself," said the woman.

"Yes, ma'am," said Janos. "O.K., ma'am," he said.

He did not make the decision at once. He waited another week before he went to her office, and he stood by the desk without speaking until she had finished what she was writing down. Then she looked up at him, the pen still in her fingers, and he cleared his throat and spoke.

"There was a question I wanted to ask you, ma'am," he said, "before I finishes making up my mind. I'd like to know if there wasn't no change yet in that question you was talking about— the colored question over there?" he said.

"No," said the woman, and she looked down at the papers underneath her hand. "I haven't been notified of any change," she said.

It was the morning after that—and Janos was not in the mess hall for breakfast—that she found the envelope, with her name printed on it, lying on her desk. Inside it were the two letters, written neatly and inaccurately on copy-book paper, and signed with Janos's name. They were not long—the first one merely four lines saying thank you and goodbye to her, and asking that she read the other letter, and send it on to Charlie Madden. The letter to Charlie Madden said:

Yessitdy I talk to the US consil Charlie and what do ya think now? Seems my fammillys jus as good as they ever waz so Charlie I make up my mynd sudden to go back whar they waz waiting for me Im shure ya thinks its for the best Charlie so I says so long

The woman sat there for a long time, holding the two letters in her hands.

The Criminal

THE FAMILY had lived since May in the pleasant, sun-filled house on the German hillside—a house that might have fitted into the setting of a shabby, obsolescent Hollywood—with long, wide windows on the south side, facing the softness of the river valley, standing a little lower than the eleventh-century castle that rose in dignity on the opposite hill, above the gray roofs of the town. Although the house had a forest behind it and a road instead of a street before it, it could not rightly be called isolated, and if the mother and father felt that it was so, it was more because every American who took part in the Occupation of this country felt within himself this sense of isolation from everything that he had known before. In the mornings, the father of the family would rub an American-brand shaving cream onto his jaw and chin and shave with blue blades, as he would have done at home, and then he would put on the same clothes and eat the same breakfast as he would have had he been catching the eight-fifteen from Scarsdale. But it was not home, and the destination was not Grand Central. The look of the world outside the windows was different, and the taste of the air when he stepped out onto the balcony was not the same. It was a former Nazi *Blockwart's* house in which the family lived, and the place to which the father drove at eight-thirty every weekday morning was Military Government buildings, with the American flag on the tall white flagstaff—where the swastika had hung once—fixed in the plot of grass before the guarded door.

The first-floor windows of the hillside house were barred, like the windows of a prison, as if the Nazi from whom the place had been requisitioned had himself feared what lay outside. But the second-floor windows, where the balconies were, were quite without protection, and because of the record of what had taken place in other houses where American families lived, the father of the family had hung the Walther pistol that he had liberated in 1945 in its leather holster by his bed, and the ammunition lay ready in the table drawer.

"There was Pritchard," the father said, telling the story to the mother soon after they came. "He'd come back from skiing in Switzerland, after Easter, and he had his right arm in plaster, having fractured it out there. It was still in plaster the night he woke up and heard someone walking around downstairs. He told his wife to stay with the baby, and he took his pistol in his left hand, and when he got halfway down the stairs, the first shot passed him." The man who had broken in had shot it out for twenty minutes with Pritchard before taking off, the father said, and neither had hit the other, but there were two holes left in one windowpane, and the mirror over the hall mantel had lost a corner where a bullet struck it. "He got away," the father said, and the children listened to the story, but without much interest. It had not happened in their time or in this house; it was somebody else's history. "He ran off through the fields, whoever he was," said the father. "In the morning, they could see his footsteps marked clearly in the dew."

There were other stories—stories the children heard or over-heard as they went about their own affairs. There was the one about another man the father had known before they came—an American called Johnson, who had a turquoise-blue Ford car. One night in April, as he drove from one town to another on the Autobahn, the headlights of his car must have picked out the figure of a man standing there with his hand raised—so the police had reconstructed it—a disreputable figure, they knew for certain, asking for a ride.

"And Johnson must have stopped, poor guy," the father said, telling the story to two Army men who were dining with them on the terrace in the dusk, "and he must have taken the German in on the seat beside him, because that's where the dead German was sitting, in his rags, when they found the wreck next day. The car had jumped the ditch and smashed head on into the iron pole of a deer-crossing sign, and Johnson himself was dead behind the wheel." The father poured fresh drinks into the officers' glasses and into the mother's glass and into his own. "But it wasn't the accident that had killed him. He'd been stabbed three times, in the ribs, as he drove, and the knife was in the German's hand still, and Johnson's wallet and papers in the inside pocket of the German's coat."

"He couldn't have had much use for them where he was going," one of the Army officers said, and the other one in uniform laughed, but there had been no sound of amusement in it
in the twilight.

"Perhaps Heaven and Hell stopped coming into their calcu-
lations a long time back," the father said in bitterness, for
Johnson had been his friend, and he didn't like the way he had
died.

It was only the children of the family who did not feel the
sense of isolation, for they were too young to miss the soda-
water fountains or the baseball games of home. Behind the
house, the woods rose, tree by tree and path by tortuous path
—leafy and murmurous, half shade, half light, all summer. It
did not matter to the children that the great stones that stood
at the entrance to the caves that had served as air-raid shelters
once were engraved with savagely hooked crosses, or that they
lived in an alien country, among alien men. For the children
shared the life of their mother and their father in this house, as
if it were a place they had chosen themselves, not knowing—
or caring, had they known—that it had been confiscated from
its owner, a man who had, in the war years, eavesdropped at
the doors of neighbors for the sound of Allied broadcasts and
turned in the names of the offenders to the local authorities.

The owner's name was there still, in brass plates on both the
front and kitchen doors, and the owner himself was not an unknown figure to the family. He could be seen from time to
time in the garden or the orchard, a heavy man wearing the
traditional Hessian gray-and-green forester's jacket, with his
white hair clipped so close on his long, tapering skull that bony
protuberances were bared below the brim of the small green
felt hat, in the space above the rosy, white-bristled rolls of

flesh that trimmed the collar of his coat. To his hatband was affixed a *Saubart*, which, even when he stooped to his work, stood upright in still glossy, still untempered arrogance. They had seen him first in May, with his heavy-limbed daughters, breaking sprays of lilac from the bushes by the front-garden gate, for, provided the current tenants did not object, it was permitted the owners of these properties to plant and tend and take the produce of the gardens that were, for the moment, no longer theirs. And the father could find no reason to object, for the *Blockwart* had had his trial and paid his fine, and when the Occupation was done, the house would again be his. So in June they saw him come for the vegetables—the radishes and lettuce and young carrots—and for the giant, drooping mauve poppies and the jasmine and peonies, and in July, with his forester's coat folded over his arm and his long, naked skull flushed red with heat, he came for the roses and red currants, and in August for the firm purple plums and the string beans, and in September, with a hand-drawn wagon, for the apples and the pears and the potatoes, while his daughters, with baskets over their arms, plucked the bunches of white grapes from the vines that hung heavy across the kitchen windows and shaded the balconies with green. Whatever the month, they left nothing of its bounty behind them—not a plum or a grape or a currant for the conquerors—bearing even the goldenrod, in great armfuls, down the dusty road.

But now the summer was through, and the children believed in another world entirely—in a world of acorns and horse chestnuts and of white-breasted squirrels flashing, red as fire, through the forest trees. In the house that belonged to them now, there were sheepnose apples from the American commissary, and peanut butter, as thick as clay, in glass jars on the pantry shelf. Not until the tall, thin man came to the basement kitchen door one morning did they think of hunger or of anyone's wanting the things they had. The man wore a torn khaki shirt and Wehrmacht trousers and a battered felt hat, of the quality of a soiled and ancient hound's ear, with the limp brim hanging low across the caverns of his eyes. He came to the kitchen door, and he asked the mother, saying some of the words in German and some in English, for the spade the owner of the house had told him was in the cellar, and as he spoke, he hitched up, with the inside of one big, bony wrist, the stained and faded trousers that wouldn't stay where they were intended to, because of the substance of his body, which hunger had hacked away. He said the owner of the house—and one soiled, thin finger pointed to the brass plaque on the door— had sent him to dig out what remained of the potatoes. The plants had already been uprooted and the best of the potatoes carried away, but he was to pick up the ones that had shaken loose in the soil, and the owner would pay him five marks for the work he did.

"Maybe he'll give me something to eat, too," he said, and there in the dark caverns of his eyes they saw the lurking thing come furtively to life and wait in trembling, bleak pain.

In the kitchen, there was the smell of eggs and bacon frying, and of cocoa warming, for the mother was making breakfast, and whether or not the children understood the words he spoke of food, they could not mistake the meaning that was in his face. To them, it seemed that if he could not have a little of what they were about to eat, then the sharp bones of his big hands and wrists would break through the useless, fleshless skin to get at what they wanted. The mother thought of the stories that had been told, and because the father was not there, she did not ask the thin man to come in. Instead, she went through the kitchen to the cellar, and she carried the spade back to him. The thin man looked at them for a moment out of the deep pits of his eyes—looking strangely, almost timidly at them—and then his long, bloodless fingers closed on the handle of the spade, and they saw him turn away.

He worked all day in the plot behind the house, turning the earth slowly, laboriously, and stooping to pick the earth-clotted potatoes out. And once, when the children passed near him, following the flight of the squirrels in the first of the forest trees, he leaned on the handle of the spade and tried to ask questions of them. Perhaps he was asking from what city they had come and by what means they had travelled, and then he seemed to speak to them of the city or country he himself had come from, for he flung his arm out toward the distance, toward places that lay beyond the river valley and beyond the yellow, wooded hills. When he saw that they did not understand his words, he made the motions of walking, bending his long, spare legs in the threadbare trousers, the boots, laced with knotted string, coming down in the same places in the earth of the potato patch, coming down over and over in dogged resolution, over and over without pause, until the children who watched him felt the weariness and the hopelessness, perhaps even recognizing for an instant the stretch of distance he had come. He worked all day, but once, in the afternoon, he took an end of black bread as small as a child's fist from his pocket and ate it, sitting with his back against a tree.

When the father drove home from work, at half past five, the man was stooping over, buckling the full bag of potatoes

closed, preparing to go. The father made the circular turn of
the drive and drove the car into the garage, and locked the
door behind him when he came out. As he walked toward the
house, he saw that the man had cleared about three-quarters
of the plot. And then, when the man stood upright, the father
saw him clearly, and his heart went sick within him—a figure
so eloquent in its suffering, so dramatically conceived, that it
might have been a portrait done in sombre oils, the dark,
despairing eyes, not of a living man but of an El Greco head,
following him now from where the canvas was placed upon
a museum's shadowy wall. It was not that he had never before seen a man so thin and so degraded by privation that any
estimates as to age, background, character, history were rendered futile; it was precisely because he had seen men like
this before that his heart went sick with an old horror, an old
fear. He had seen them in 1945, in Dachau, when he and the
other Americans had come in—skeletons that had seemed to
rise from the heaps of them in the courtyard but that were
somehow still-living men, ageless, pastless, coiling the rope
in the claws of their hands to hang the S.S. guards who had
not been able to get away. And none of the Americans had
moved to stop them; even the father had stood, bearing witness to murder, with his head bowed in contrition and humil-
ity. As the man passed beyond him along the strip of frost-
yellowed, withered grass, the father opened his mouth as if
to speak to him, but he did not speak. Instead, he stood silently
there, filled with a nameless emotion, watching the man go.

At seven in the morning, when the mother went downstairs
to put the coffee on, she saw what had taken place. A wild
wind had seemingly blown through the dining room and the
sitting room, carrying all things before it, blasting the drawers

and doors of the sideboards and tables and cupboards open and sweeping them bare. All that had lain in order within them— silver and linen, checker and chess and domino sets, bills, papers, maps, telephone books, and sewing materials—was there in chaos upon the floor. For an instant, the mother stood motionless, trying to make some sense of it all.

Do you mean this happened, do you mean the children did this when they went to look for the package of pretzels before going to bed, she asked herself in bewilderment, and then she saw that the pane in one of the sitting-room windows had been cut away.

The father came down in his pajamas when she called, and the children awoke and came, too, standing there without slippers and shivering with pleasure at the sight of this anonymous disorder, this chaos and disruption in which they had played no part.

"He didn't take my cigarette case," was the first thing the father said. It was lying with the scattered letters, the newspapers, the carbon and typewriting paper on the floor, lying open, with the cigarettes gone from it, and the father stooped and picked it up. "Sterling silver," he said, a little ruefully, "but he didn't want it," and he snapped it closed.

"He wanted the cigarettes, but he wanted something else," the mother said, and she picked her way through the hopeless clutter of objects that, it seemed, might never find their proper place.

"My stamp collection," the father said, in true concern.

"Perhaps your passport. It was in the desk," the mother said quietly, and they both sought among the confusion of books and papers and photographs a moment. The albums of the stamp collection lay under the litter, unharmed, and the passport, in its cellophane cover, was there. All through the rooms was a trail of burned-out matches, testifying that the man had carried no flashlight with him, and here and there was the darkening print of blood. The mark of blood was on the dining-room silver, which he had emptied out onto the table, not daring to take it, perhaps, because of the monogram on it, or else not wanting that at all. And the blood was there on the salmon-colored brocaded tablecloth, which they kept for dinner parties, and on the napkins, still folded corner-wise but marked with red, and there was blood on the wicker of the sewing basket, for he had overturned it in his haste and then made some effort to stuff the contents back in it again. But he had not wanted the scissors or the silver thimble or the skeins of wool it held. "It was something else," said the mother—not the crystal liqueur glasses, which he had touched, leaving the four or five charred, twisted matches beside them once he had viewed them in their beauty, and not the silver ashtrays or the napkin rings, which his fingertips had clouded when he picked them up. "It was something else he wanted," the mother said.

The instrument with which he had cut the pane out lay, as idle as a paperweight now, on the pile of disorder on the sitting-room table—an iron tool, staple-shaped and evil, with one dull, broken end and the other end filed as fine as a strong needle, with the tip worn white from the work of cutting it had done. The father picked it up and studied it a moment.

"This is the kind of thing that is used to grapple logs together when they float them down a river. Perhaps he came down the valley with logs. Perhaps he came from a long way off," the father said.

In the hall, he had not touched the hunting rifles, which

hung on the coat hooks, or the binoculars or the optical sights. He had been looking for something else, something that was not to be found in the ground-floor bathroom, either, for the new cakes of soap and the razor, in its imitation-leather box, had not been taken, although he had touched the razor for an instant, for the trace of blood was there. It was only when they went down the cement stairs to the kitchen, where he had passed the two pairs of the father's shoes on the shoe rack, and not taken them for his own, that they understood what he had been after. The refrigerator door stood open, and the mother went at once to it, but the shelves looked as burdened as they had before. The uncooked chicken and the uncooked joint of beef were there, and the eggs and the bottles of beer, and the bottles of good Danish milk. He had taken nothing but a half pound of butter from the icebox shelf. They followed the way he had gone by the trail of burned-out matches left behind him, and in the storeroom, having struck match after match and studied the labels by their light, he had found the things that he wanted to take away.

"Just what he could eat on the side of the road somewhere," the mother said. But he hadn't been able to wait that long; they found the paper of a half-pound bar of unsweetened baking chocolate on the floor, where he had dropped it, empty.

"Oh, God, he must have been hungry to eat that!" the father said.

He had taken two cans of sardines—and left them two—and the smallest can of frankfurters, and a half-size can of salmon and one of shrimp. From the kitchen-table drawer, he had taken one knife and a can opener, and from the bread-box a loaf of raisin bread.

"He took only what he needed for the road," the mother

said, and the "he" indicated a man who had walked for a long time, and who would go on walking, as explicitly as if her suspicion had spoken a proper name.

Whoever he was, he had gone out through the cellar door, leaving it open behind him, and as the mother and father stood there looking out across the orchard, they could see the marks of footsteps in the deep, cold dew. They believed then that they could see him going, accepting without question, and with a certain sense of guilt and sorrow, that it should be he. They could see the great, bony shoulders stooped, the wilted felt hat drooping low about his ears, the string-tied boots scarring their way across the orchard grass.

"It would have been less trouble for him to have rung the bell last night and asked for food," said the father, his voice irritable with his own shame.

"He must be a long way off by this time," the mother said.

But, just after eight, there he was in the potato patch again, taking up the work where he had left off, slowly and wearily spading the earth away. The maid had come, and she and the mother were in the kitchen, busying themselves with the setting of the place in order, and the father had gone out the door to take the car from the garage when he saw the skeleton, in a long coat this time, at work in the misty morning air. So the father dropped his bunch of keys into his pocket, and he crossed the drive and went up the stretch of sloping ground. The coat that the thin man wore came almost to his ankles, a coat that a German officer had worn once—rusty and greenish, with a braid-edged velvet collar and high, smart, flaring lapels.

"*Guten Tag*," the father said, and the man looked up from under the hanging brim of his hat. Oh, God! thought the father, the sharpness of the pain returning. That look that men have the power to put into one another's eyes!

"*Guten Tag*," the thin man answered, and his voice was gentle, but it was clear that he was not convinced of the truth of the words he had just said.

"You're a stranger to this part of the country, aren't you?" the father said, speaking German still. The Army coat that the thin man wore had certainly never been his, for the sleeves rode halfway up his bony arms, and although there could be no question of buttoning it across, still, even as it hung open, the breadth of his carcass had split its seams.

"Yes," said the man. He had thrust the spade upright into the soil, and his big-wristed forearms hung motionless now from the too short, too tight frayed velvet cuffs of the sleeves. "I've been walking three weeks. I'm working my way to Fulda," he said.

"You've been doing some work with lumber, bringing trees downstream?" asked the father in his quite presentable German.

"Yes," the man said again, and the lurking, ailing thing that the children had seen in the deep pits of his eyes looked warily at the man who stood, in his good clothes, before him. "I've been doing anything I could get," he said, and he lowered his head and shifted on his feet, dragging the cadaver of his destitution a little nearer to the father in the cold.

"Look," said the father, speaking firmly, "you come over to the house with me." The man followed him down the slope of frost-burned grass and across the drive and onto the pavings of the terrace, following in the half-helpless, half-eager acquiescence with which a well-disciplined dog comes to heel. The father opened the front door of the house with his latch-key, and the thin man in the comic-opera overcoat followed him in and wiped his feet, as the father had, on the mat inside the door. As they crossed the hall, the father could hear the mingled voices of the mother and children and the maid, below them, in the kitchen, speaking quickly, with excitement, among themselves. The father led the man through the sitting room, past the chaos of papers on the table and the floor, through the disorder of the dining room, and out onto the balcony, and he asked him to stand there. The man had taken his hat off, in respect, as he came into the house, and when the father went back through the dining room alone and into the sitting room, he could see the macabre figure framed by the broken windowpane standing abjectly, obediently, on the balcony, under the dry ropes of the grapevine, with his head bare in the wash of the morning sun. The man's hair was sparse, and high on his big, domed forehead there was a violent scar that slashed into his scalp, marking a crescent of white, waxlike flesh, hairless and nearly opalescent, above one bloodless ear. The father looked at him for a moment, and then he picked up the iron grapple from the table where it lay, and as he walked toward the window, he did not take his eyes from the man who stood on the balcony, beyond the broken glass. "Here," the father said quietly, and he put his hand, with the iron grapple in it, through the opening in the pane. "Take this," he said. "Show me how it was done."

The man's eyes shifted toward the sound of his voice, and when he saw the father extending the grapple to him, he crossed the stone of the balcony with a humble, eager step. He took the instrument from the father's hand and he looked at it curiously a moment, not as if it were a strange thing to him but as if seeking to determine how it happened to be here. Then his eyes focussed slowly on the father, standing on the other side of the glass.

"Like this. It was done like this," he said. He had sought for and found the sharp end of the grapple, and now the point of it was raised, and he looked at the father eagerly. He seemed to feel that by showing a wholly cooperative spirit he could establish his right of belonging to the father's side. "The point was put in here," he said, his face gone sober with interest as he fitted it to the broken edge. "And then, with the weight put against it, and turning it all the time, the glass would be cut out," he said, and the point of the grapple followed the arc down. "You have to do it over and over, with great care," he said, "and then the glass will give."

"And then, when the piece of glass is gone, you just pass your hand in through the opening and turn the handle and open the window," the father said, speaking quietly to the thin man. "But in the dark you might cut your hand doing it," he said.

"Yes," said the man. "You'd put your hand in like this," he said, and he laid the grapple down on the stone of the window sill and passed his right hand inside and felt for the handle. When he did this, the father saw the cut on the yellowish flesh of his palm.

"So. Now tell me," the father said, speaking just as quietly as before, "how long did it take you to cut the glass out?" And his fingers closed strongly around the big, flat bones of the thin man's wrist.

"How long?" asked the man. With his wrist caught there, as if in a trap, in the father's fingers, he seemed to reflect on it a moment. "Perhaps an hour, perhaps two hours. You have to go very carefully," he said, and then the look that had been wiped from his eyes came back, and the tracked and circumvented beast lay waiting in the sunken pits. "Who, me? Not me!" he said, and he ran his tongue along his lip. "I didn't do it. I didn't have anything to do with it. I wasn't here last night," he said.

"Come in," the father said. His fingers let the man's wrist go, and he motioned to the balcony door. The man turned slowly and crossed the balcony, and he came through the dining room, walking slowly, abjectly, in the German Army officer's coat, through the disorder and into the sitting room, where the father stopped. "Sit down," the father said, and when he was seated, the father sat down on the other side of the table and he held a packet of cigarettes out to him. "What's your trade?" the father said.

"I'm a salesman, a shoe salesman," the man said. His fingers were shaking as he took the cigarette, and even in his mouth it shook as the father held a light to it. "I'll be all right if I can get to Fulda," he said. "I have an uncle and some cousins there."

"Where did you sleep last night?" said the father, lighting his own cigarette.

"I slept in a tool shed in one of the vegetable gardens down the road," the thin man said, and as the father studied him across the faint blue vapor of smoke, his eyes fled bleakly through the room.

"And the hunger got bad. It got a little worse than it was before," said the father, drawing slowly, deeply, on his cigarette, "and so you came up here."

"No," said the man. "It was the first night in three weeks I had a roof over me. I went to sleep."

"Oh, Christ!" said the father, leaning forward. "Don't you think I'd understand it? Do you think I'd judge you for it?" he said impatiently. "How low do you think the human being can sink, to what depths of censure and condemnation do you

think the human being can go? Tell me any story you like
about the cut on your hand," he said in a kind of fury. "It
doesn't matter! It's past a matter of telling the truth or telling a lie, or recognizing the truth if you heard it. You're dying
on your feet, starved, famished, discussing ethics with a man
who's eaten. . . ."

The skeleton sat looking strangely, uneasily, at him, not
certain whether this was anger or not, not comprehending
what the father was seeking to say. And then the doorbell rang
sharply out, and the father jumped to his feet, as nervously
as if his name had been called aloud. He went out of the sitting
room and downstairs quickly and opened the front door.
There, in his Hessian forester's jacket, stood the owner of
the house, holding the hat with the *Saubart* in it in his handsomely gloved hands. He stood there somewhat obsequiously,
somewhat like a trespasser, at the threshold of his own front
door, his shoulders back but the white-bristled skull tilted as
if in apology. Beneath the forester's jacket, the father saw that
the *Blockwart* wore a shirt of soft-gray flannel and that his
shoes—beneath the knife pleats of the gray Loden trousers—
were obviously American-made, black-market, new.

"*Guten Tag*," the *Blockwart* said, and as the father looked
at the officious, the fiercely bigoted face, he was filled with a
wild, unreasoning anger, an almost unbearable fury, at the
sight of the corpulent, rosy flesh before him, and the handsome, traditional clothes.

"What is it you want here?" he shouted, and it came to him
that this was the first time they had ever come so close or
looked into each other's eyes.

"I beg your pardon for the intrusion," the *Blockwart* said,
tilting his naked head, "but I came up to pay the man who was

getting my potatoes out, and your servant tells me it is possible he broke into the house last night. It is a mistake to deal with anyone who hasn't a roof over his head, and I should not have done so," he said, but it was almost as if he were catching the father up on some negligence. "I feel a certain responsibility for his being here. A certain responsibility," he repeated. "I see the spade and bag out there, and I believe you are questioning him. I would be quite willing to relieve you of the matter and turn him over to the police myself," he said.

"No," said the father, speaking carefully. "You can't do that. He isn't the man."

"Not the man?" said the *Blockwart* sharply, and it might have been an order that he gave. "But it must be the man!" he said, and it behooved them now to jerk their chins up as they faced each other, bring their heels together, clap their arms, rigid, by their sides.

"There is no indication that he is the man." The father confirmed it. "His hand is not cut, while the man who broke in left blood on everything." And then he closed the door.

The *Blockwart's* clock in the hall was just striking nine when the father walked back into the sitting room, and the thin man was sitting on the edge of the armchair still, smoking nervously at his cigarette. "Come on downstairs and have some breakfast," said the father, and the skeleton did not look at him but drew his bones together and got up painfully. As he and the father went down the stairs, to the sound of the women's and children's voices, the father said, "I'll drive you to the station afterward and put you on a train. You'll get to Fulda quicker that way."

216

Adam's Death

T HE VILLAGE the American car stopped in, one late summer afternoon, was off the highroad, in that part of Germany designated as Land Hesse. There could not have been more than fifty or sixty houses in the village, and a square-towered church, which seemed, in its austerity, vowed to relinquish nothing either to the grace of the rolling wooded country or to the homage of erring man. The young woman who drove the car had brought it to a tentative stop near the church, on a cobbled square at the edge of a grassy common. From opposite sides of the square, the village road wound off among blocks of strong farmhouses, a road so still that wisps of hay from wagons that had passed lay unstirring—untrodden, even

—on it, as if on the broad boards of a quiet loft. From where she sat in the car, the young woman could discern no sign of the living on the village thoroughfare, except for a line of geese that moved along it, proceeding, as if through alternating shallow and deep water, through the areas of sun and shade. The birds were tall, and their bodies, their throats, their wings were a clear, unsullied white. But beauty such as swans possess they had none of, thought the woman, and she watched them pass from sun to shadow, shadow to sun, in stiff-necked bigotry.

Beside her in the car there sat a boy of four or five, with hair as black as her hair, and eyes set deeply, as her eyes were set, beneath dark, delicate brows. For a moment after they stopped, he did not speak, but sat looking out through the lowered glass of the car door at the green of the common, on which school children played. "There're children here, too," he said then, in his high, eager voice.

"Yes," said his mother quickly. "But if we stayed here, you'd simply have to not play with the children."

"But I like to play with children," he said, not turning his head from the sight of them on the grass.

"I know," said his mother, and she looked down at her hands as she spoke. "We've talked about this before." There was no way to say to him that every morning on waking, in the city they had left, the fear with which one had gone to sleep at night was present still, still unallayed, dissolving the mind with panic. "If you got ill, then perhaps you would never be able to play again," she said. A red suède bag lay in her lap, and in it, with her monogrammed cigarette case, her tasselled lipstick, her expensive compact, was a typed report card from his American nursery school. It was headed

"Darmfurt, Germany," and it covered July and a portion of August, and beneath the information dealing with place and time and the boy's identity was noted: "Satisfactory progress, although he is still shy, quiet, and has little to say. He seems to enjoy all our activities in his own way, and is most coopera- tive." "You see . . ." his mother began to say, but she did not go on with it. Even a first-grade primer had no words simple enough to say to him that in the hospitals of the ruined city they had left children lay stricken, stricken and dying, paraly- sis turning their arms and their legs and their lungs to stone. She sat looking down at her hands, thinking: You see, if you die, you can't enjoy activities. Death isn't cooperative. It isn't cooperative at all.

For two weeks, she had thought of flight, had talked of it with the boy's father—of flight from the city, leaving the fear, the menace, to other mothers, other children, giving them, as a parting gift to keep forever, the hospital beds, the tortured limbs, the strangling breath; believing, in instants of savagery, that she loved or feared more hopelessly than other mothers loved or feared. And here they were now—out of the city, and away from the river valley and from whatever threat the river water bore. Beyond, farther down the road, a bracketed iron *Gasthaus* sign hung above one of the cobbled-courtyard gates, the single word of refuge done in Gothic script and the harplike strokes of it painted black and gold. The houses were bound by heavy, oil-stained beams, and within this frame- work strong transverse timbers slashed right and left across the massive whitewashed walls.

"These Germans must have been good Germans. They didn't smash their houses all up, the way the Germans in the city did," the boy said.

"Maybe it will be better here," said the mother. "Maybe it won't be like Germany any more."

She opened the door of the car and pushed aside the books that lay on the big, soft cushions of the seat before she stepped down upon the stones. There were four books. Three of them, in new glazed-paper jackets—*Mrs. Dalloway*, with a special introduction by the author; *The Portable James Joyce;* and *The Portable Faulkner*—could be found on Post Exchange book counters, and usually were left lying there. The fourth book was a child's book, shaped like a Greyhound bus, and the faces of passengers were visible at the painted windows of it, and the wheels were cardboard and actually turned.

At the craftily curtained windows of the village houses, there were no faces to be seen—only potted geraniums, red and pink and white, lending the miniature panes a look of innocence. But still the eyes of the old and of other women must have watched from behind them as the young American woman came down the street, slender, small-featured, alert, with varnish as red as blood on her fingernails, and lipstick brilliant on her mouth. The eyes must have censured the bizarre print dress, the red suède shoes, seeing in peasant outrage or uproarious peasant mirth her tanned, naked legs and her arms bare from the shoulder, and the pagan silver bracelets moving at her wrists—and seen, but with pity for him, because of their abomination of her, the boy in faded corduroys who walked beside her, holding the nameless creature's thin, restless hand. But there was no stir behind the windows; there was no whisper of this other life. The air was still, the doors were closed, and from the lofts that stood open beneath the overhanging eaves came the smell of the new hay.

The woman who opened the door of the *Gasthaus* to them

wore the Hessian dress, with the heavy skirt of it reaching below her ankles, and her hair, in the local peasant manner, was
wrenched up sharply from her swollen brow. The American
woman could speak a little German, and she told the *Gasthaus*
keeper's wife that she wanted a room with two beds in it,
where she and her little boy could stay for a while. As the
woman mounted the dark wood stairs before them, there was
a wariness in the set of her narrow shoulders, and when they
stood in the big, clean room together, it was there in the side
of her face, in the small, close, cautious ear, the guarded eye.
The ceiling was white and low, and the posts of the painted
bedsteads seemed tall enough for the ceiling to rest upon them.
The bedposts were a primal blue in color, with flowers stencilled on them in clear yellow, red, and green. Between the
posts billowed the soft, deep feather beds, buttoned into
starched envelopes, bloated with plumage, and immacuately
white.

"Let's live here," the boy said, but the *Gasthaus* keeper's
wife was not at all sure that they would be worth the trouble
they would give. She moved across the wide boards of the
floor to the doll-sized window, where the midget curtain hung,
and with the side of her hand she brushed the crisp little bodies
of dead wasps from the window sill.

The American woman laid her handbag down on the white-
clothed table, as if accepting this now as the place where they
would stay. She said that twice in the week she would drive
back to the city for food, for American food bought at the
commissary—for coffee and rice and sugar and fat, for meat
and flour and cereals—and the *Gasthaus* keeper's wife took
this for the terms of an agreement proffered, and she slowly
shook her head.

"The payment would have to be in Deutschmarks," she said, the wary eye averted. "We have these other things."

"But for us to eat—for the boy and me to eat—so that we wouldn't take your food from you," the mother said quickly.

"Deutschmarks," said the woman, in her simple Hessian dress. She said that when her husband came in from the fields, the American woman would have to talk with him. It was not for her, who was herself merely woman, to tell them whether to go or stay.

"Would you rather be rich or would you rather be hot?" the little boy asked his mother as they followed her down the *Gasthaus* stairs.

"Well, perhaps rich—rich rather than hot," said his mother, with her mind not on it.

"But if you were rich, then you might be hot, too. If you got into a place where there was fire, then you'd have to be hot," the little boy said, and now that they had followed the woman into the *Gasthaus* kitchen, it might have been the room he was speaking of.

The air was tart to smell there, and the little windowpanes were misted, because of the pots of blue plums cooking on the stove. There were other women there, women older than the *Gasthaus* keeper's wife, sitting working at the table, their skirts as heavy as winter coats, and coarse white kerchiefs tied across their heads. They picked the plums out of the baskets held on their knees, and they split the fruit lengthwise with their knives and cut the flat, brown, pointed stones away. The mother saw that their strong, seamed hands were stained from the flesh of the plums they touched, and she saw, as well, that their wrinkled cheeks were sucked inward, drawn tight as silk across their empty gums, as they looked at the half-clothed stranger who had sat down apart from them on a wooden bench and put her arm around the boy. And then in her uncertain German she put the question to them.

"Perhaps you could tell me," she said, "if there are any children ill here—here in the village?" She looked from one to the other of their faces, asking it of them in fear.

"Ill?" said the *Gasthaus* keeper's wife, glancing up from the vessel of plums she was stirring on the stove. "Any children ill?" she said. Near her, on the kitchen dresser, stood a wide-throated pitcher brimming with milk, and three great wheels of country bread, and butter in a crockery dish. Just behind the pitcher of milk could be seen a carton of Camel cigarettes, and four brightly lettered little tins of G. Washington instant coffee, but the mother was not thinking of these things. She was looking at the women's faces, asking this urgent question of their impervious eyes. "Any children ill here in the village?" the *Gasthaus* keeper's wife repeated, and once the other women had shaken their heads, she said "Nay" to the mother, across the vapor of the cooking plums.

But even after the *Gasthaus* keeper had come and talked to the American woman, on the wood steps in the sun, there was still no satisfactory explanation of why she had come to the village with the boy. She said that her husband was stationed in Darmfurt, but to them, whom the Occupation had scarcely touched, this was almost without meaning. Darmfurt, they had been told, was no more than an agglomeration of ruins now, but whatever it was, it lay two hundred kilometres outside the confines of their curiosity. And currency was what he wanted, currency he had to have, so the mother paid the Deutschmarks to him for the first week they would stay. Like his wife, he set aside the talk of bringing food to them; the

potato crop was good this year, he said, standing there squint-
ing into the courtyard's warm summer light, a swarthy, thick-
shouldered, straight-backed man, savoring the prosperous flavor of the things he said. A neighbor who had bought a cow
from him had paid him partly in cocoa, partly in sugar.

"Jack Frost, granulated," he specified. While the village
baker, who owed him for the rent of pasture land, had paid
his debt to him in flour. "Gold Medal, much finer grained
than German flour," the *Gasthaus* keeper said. "Every week,
they'll come past your door with soap and rice and coffee to
sell," he went on. "I'll buy when the rice is Carolina glazed
and the coffee is in tins, not bags. My wife wants the soap that
comes in paper wrappers. Octagon, when they have that,"
he said.

He said they would kill a pig next week, in a private way,
not bringing the government regulations into it, and he said
there would be plenty of poppy oil to see them through the
winter, and as he talked of it, he reached a bouquet of dried
poppyheads down from where they hung, their parched stems
knotted with raffia, from the beam above the open door. Then
he stooped, and with his blunt, earth-bitten fingers he made a
cup of the boy's hand, and, still stooping, he tapped the indigo
poppy seeds into the hollow of it out of the split, papery pod.

"But where do they come from—the rice, the soap, the coffee?" the mother said.

"Well, the *Amis* over here have so much they have to get
rid of it. Overproduction in America," the *Gasthaus* keeper
said. "If they don't keep it moving around the world, then
the selling price will drop below the cost of producing, and
then they'll have inflation. That's how it is." He stood up, and
he brushed the rest of the poppy seeds from his work-worn

hands. "They're full of oil. They'll fatten him up," said the
Gasthaus keeper, and the boy looked up at his mother before
he tried them on his tongue.

The first evening they were there, the mother and boy followed along a deeply rutted wagon road together, leaving the
houses of the village and the unrelenting tower of the church
behind. The road led away through fields and pastures toward
the dark regions of the forest, drawing them onward under
the pure, unbroken arch of sky or evening, through the clarity
and stillness, toward the equivocal forest, as the lingering
afternoon itself had drawn them hour after hour toward the
night.

"Why is the sky all around? When will the stars come?"
the boy asked, his voice as fragile as glass on the clear, still
evening air. But the mother and boy spoke little as they
walked, perhaps hushed in trepidation of the myriad life of
the woods that lay in mystery before them. "Maybe there'll
be wild pigs there," the boy said, remembering that once in
the spring his father had left the city to hunt them by moonlight in the hills. "Maybe there'll be elephants," he said.

On one side of the road, a stream ran, its passage muted by
the long, fresh grasses that flowed within its bed. And on the
other side lay the fields planted with winter turnips, their
leaves, thought the mother, like Rousseau's strong, lacquered
jungle leaves. Beneath this lustrous emerald foliage, the wax-
white turnips shouldered their way out of the soil.

"We may see deer come out of the woods," said the mother,
and then she glanced to the side of the road on which the
stream ran, and she saw the other, the unexpected, thing that
stood there just beyond the wagon ruts, in the beginning of
the grass. It was nothing more than a stone—a smooth stone

shaped like the head board of a bed—but there could be no mistaking the meaning of it. It was a gravestone, its presence stating that life had ended here.

The boy had picked up a spray of leaves from the foot of a tree they had passed, and now he struck at the weeds with it as he walked ahead. But the mother had halted, and she stepped nearer in the deepening light to read the letters and numbers inscribed on the stone. "*Adam's Tod, 1944,*" it said, and below it the curved delicate blade of a scythe had been engraved.

"Adam's death," the mother said under her breath, and it seemed to her suddenly then that all they had fled from might come this far to reach them, might pursue them and outstrip them here. "Adam's death," she repeated, scarcely aloud, and she shivered as if the cold had touched her. "Darling, come back!" she called out in panic to the boy. "It's getting late! Tomorrow we'll go as far as the forest. We'll start out earlier," she said, and, switching the weeds and flower heads as he came, the boy turned back to her from the engulfing tide of dark.

But the next day it rained, and they did not go out, and the day after that the accident took place. A peasant passed by the *Gasthaus* riding a bicycle slowly, bringing along behind him a strong gray mare on a halter as he rode. And behind the mare, or beside her, or else cavorting ahead, came a slim black colt, the fruit of her loins, without bridle or rope, making a show of freedom but tethered to her by love. He was so shy that when pigeons winged up from a courtyard, his supple neck arched like a hunter's bow and his unshod hoofs stamped on the cobbles, but he had a certain kind of giddy humor in his eyes as he skidded from one side of the village road to the other. From the *Gasthaus* doorway, the boy and the mother saw the colt, with his nostrils lipping the shimmering, rain-washed air and his muscles running swift as water within his hide, and the boy went leaping out the *Gasthaus* gate and followed the colt in speechless pleasure, lowering his head and moving as the young horse moved, thin and awkward and somehow brother to the colt, with one eye on his mother, as the colt's eye was on the mare. And then, just before the turn in the road, the boy fell and struck his mouth upon the stones. The peasant wheeling slowly on the bicycle, the mare, the colt, did not pause, not merely not spectators to it but as if they were not on the same unfolding length of film on which this had occurred. Their own complete procession, in perfected Technicolor, flickered a little longer, until they made the turn, on the screen of alternating sun and shade.

Two of the village women brought the mother a towel to hold to the boy's split mouth, and she held it against the blood, the mud, the dung, the violent screams, in her wild, trembling hands.

"To the doctor, the doctor!" one of the peasant women cried out, and from the doorways and courtyards and lofts other voices shouted it aloud. But the doctor had ridden off on a truckload of plums, to sell them to wholesalers in the Kreis, the postman said, and he looked at the boy and shook his head. "To the dentist, to the dentist, then!" the voices altered it, and one of the women ran ahead to show the mother the way.

It was far; it was nearly half a mile to the dentist's house, for he lived on the outskirts of the village, beyond the last of the strong peasant houses, on the very brink of the sun-drenched open land. And as they mounted the footpath to the dentist's house at last, the sight of the village and the sound of its people were left behind, and now there were larks that sang above them, and it might have been that a door had been flung wide to the freshness of the fields and the clear, bright metal of the shining air. It was perhaps this vision of the expanding country, lustrous with rich grasses and melodious streams, that made the boy cease his choking crying, so that they mounted in silence between the fragrant banks of deep, wet clover to the dentist's door.

It was nothing more than a chicken house that he lived in, with salvaged squares and patches of tin nailed to the boards to spare it from the weather. The roof was flat, and there was a rusted pipe thrust through it to serve as chimney, and the bits of timber that had been used to fashion the window frames had seemingly been split from packing crates for this purpose no longer than a day or two before. But on the home-made door the dentist's shingle hung, the letters stencilled in black on a white ground, professionally, neatly done, like that of a well-established practitioner. "Dr. Eli Jacobi, Zahnarzt, Universität Saarbrücken," the letters said to the trembling silence of the country, and the mother still held the blood-soaked towel to the boy's mouth as she knocked on the door.

When the mother told the story, afterward, she could not explain to herself how the thing that had come to matter then was not what had happened to the boy. The facts themselves were simple enough: the boy had split his two front upper teeth in the fall, and the dentist, once he had sponged the blood and filth away, had done expertly, with decision, what there was to do. But the issue—the crisis, even—was something else, something that dealt with the boy no longer but with strangers, something so alien that one could not put one's finger on its name. The dentist had injected Novocain into the lacerated gum, and the boy had not cried out in protest as the needle slid in; he had not moved in protest or pain when the dentist took out the splintered teeth, shielding the pincers from the boy's sight, as he had the needle, with the back of his long hand.

"You see, the roots seem long—long for a child's first teeth," Dr. Jacobi said, speaking a slow, heavy English to the mother. "That is because the teeth had not made their preparations to come out," he said, and he spread the bits and slivers of them on his palm. Dr. Jacobi was a short, thin, soft-looking man, white as a slug—a man of forty, or even older, the mother decided. His crimped red hair receded from a tenuous point of gold above his forehead, his nose was white and prominent, his nostrils were curved, and he had an anxious, light-lashed eye. "So now he must remain so—three or four years so, namely—without these teeth, until the two new ones come down," he said.

But the heart of the story was not this; it had nothing to do with a boy's courage or a man's precision. It did not reside in the fact that a piano stood in one corner of the single, un-partitioned room, or that a framed photograph of an Epstein sculpture hung above it, at a height at which barnyard fowl must have perched in sleep in this place once, out of the reach of fox and rat and weasel, huddled close in terror when the stench of their coming troubled the dark, stale air. Nor was it the books of music that lay open—the Gershwin and Stravin-sky scores, the yellowing sheets of Mozart's and Purcell's com-posing—that gave another meaning to what had taken place. The story was contained in a pencil drawing hanging above the covered couch that served Dr. Jacobi as a bed, and on

which he had bidden the boy lie down and rest. It was a drawing of a rutted wagon road, the wheel and hoof prints upon it,
the grasses that grew long beside it, done sharply and with
artistry. By the side of the road, a stone stood clear of the
grass, and on the stone *"Adam's Tod, 1944"* was inscribed,
and below this a scythe blade was curved.

"Who did that drawing?" the mother asked in a quick,
low voice of wonder. She was seated beside the couch where
the boy lay, nearly asleep.

"I made it. I drew it," Dr. Jacobi said, his bloodless face
gone sharp. He was cleaning his instruments quietly and putting them away, and now he, too, looked up at the drawing on
the boards of the chicken-house wall. "I came here eight
months ago," he said, and as if this were some kind of explanation, "having graduated a little late from university.
I came here, to this village that had no dentist, to set out in
my professional career. A little late," he repeated, saying it
bitterly, ironically. "My studies were interrupted," he said,
and he turned to the cleaning of his instruments again.

"So then you didn't know the man called Adam? You didn't
know who he was?" the mother said. The boy slept now, and
she held his helpless, pliant fingers in her hand.

And then, in amazement, she sensed anger in the dentist's
gesture as he flung the instruments aside, and his breath and
his step were quick with impatience as he came to where she
sat beside the sleeping boy.

"Ah, yes, I knew him! Don't make any mistake! I knew
him!" he cried out, and she saw the passion that had darkened
and transformed his soft pale face. "I knew him alive, or men
so like him that I can say I knew him, even if I came here four
years after he died. I knew him in Auschwitz, in Buchenwald;

we were together in every ghetto of Europe together—men so like him or so like myself that we could be taken one for the other! Adam!" he cried out, and his yellowish eyes blazed at the seated woman. "Just Adam! No more than that! My brother or your brother, your son or mine, lying dead under a stone by the side of the road!" He ran one long finger inside the collar of his shirt, and he cleared his throat savagely, as if seeking to free his voice of the wild emotion that held it fast. "Everyone knew him here—all the village people," he went on, more quietly, then. "They put up the stone for him. They did that much. But the peasants speak of him to me when they come here with their aching teeth, for he still lies heavy on their conscience, the village conscience. Sometimes it seems to me that they come not because of the pains in their teeth but because of the words they want to speak of him and do not know how to say. Because once they knew a man who did something for them for nothing, one man without a name, a refugee, asking nothing of them except the right to stay alive. Just once!" he said, speaking in irony and bitterness of the peasants who stood strong as oak, as rock, about them, embedded in the soil. "They say he came from Berlin—in 1933 or 1934, it was—but they do not say he was fleeing in terror from what was there. He came and he worked their fields for them, slept with their cattle, ate with their swine. Adam!" Dr. Jacobi cried out, his passion rising again. "One man they didn't have to drive a bargain with!"

"And then he died. He died on the wagon road," the mother said, scarcely aloud.

"Yes, yes, he died," said the dentist, nearly master of himself again, and he drew one shaking hand across his crimpy hair. "They cannot tell you if it was an accident, or if he died by his own or by another man's hand. The peasants found him by the road one evening, dead in a lake of blood, killed by the scythe with which he had been cutting the long grass in their fields all day. It had entered his belly," the dentist said, making the gesture, "and come out through his spine, and when they lifted him, they tell me his body was as light as a little child's. Because he had not eaten well," he said, his tongue tip running along his lip. "I ask them when they come here, and I cannot find a man who ever asked him to sit down at his table. He did not sit down and eat with men and women in the ten years he was here. And perhaps sometimes he lays his hand on their hearts in dreams at night, and that wakes them, for there are days when they come uneasily to me and ask me if he had had more flesh to cover his bones, would he have died so quickly by the roadside, or they ask me if they should put a cross upon his stone."

Dr. Jacobi turned away and finished cleaning his instruments then, and the mother did not speak, and after a while the boy stirred and woke, and then they rose to go. It was not easy to bring herself to speak of money, but she did this as he stood by the chicken-house door, and at the sound of her words the quality of strength or pride or reticence he had was taken from him, as if his manhood were taken from him, and he looked away.

"Not money," he said. "You see, a country dentist cannot ask much—one mark or two. It is never enough to pay for what they have to sell. But if I could ask you—that is, if you could bring me something else, not now, but when it is available. . . ."

The mother looked at the hollow side of his face for an instant before she understood. It was perhaps the nearly per-

ceptible outline of the teeth within the jaw that made it un-
mistakably clear.

"Food?" she said in a low voice, and when Dr. Jacobi turned
his head quickly, she saw the bright, violent light of hope that
burned now in his eyes.

"Yes, food," he said. "Whatever you could spare." And
there was nothing more to say.

Aufwiedersehen Abend

IT WOULD be possible to divide them into two nearly equal categories, the American civilians who came to work in Germany. There were those who came because of the varying ways and means of profit, or the illusion of power, which this Occupation employment offered; and there were those who had returned to what had been their homeland once, American citizens now, but still German enough to believe that they alone could draw near to, and perhaps cure, the country's ailing heart. The odd ones, who fitted under neither of these two heads, might be disposed of as fanatics. Some of them were young men who had left Stateside colleges to fight the war, and who had learned in mud, and blood, and combat, a lesson so violent that they had no patience left for classroom or campus. They had severed themselves from their home towns, and their people, and the girls they would go back and marry in the end, and for a second time they had come to this country, but not as soldiers, not in uniform, but as civilians with a mission, having accepted both war and peace as their responsibility.

One of these men, one of this odd minority, was a young man named Rod Murray, who had come out of the Midwest on the common errand of reorientation, come seeking the look of sincerity in other men's faces, and the sound of truth in their voices when they described the roles that they had played. He had been a bomber pilot once, and now his name, and his title as Information Services Officer, were stencilled on an office door in a building designated as American Military Government in an ancient university town. The town, with its *Schloss*, and its medieval halls of learning, stood solidly and picturesquely, built to outlast all wars, it seemed, and all orientation, upon a Hessian hillside. When the work of the day was over, and the Military Government offices closed, Rod Murray did not go back to his billets to play poker with the others, and he did not sit in a movie hall with his arm around a *Fräulein*, because this quest for the freedom-loving and the enlightened could know no respite until it had reached some kind of end. The name of love might have been given to this search, but it was more dedicated than any pursuit of woman, this fateful seeking in an alien country for men with whom free men might have affinity. Rod Murray could be seen of an evening in the town hall of one or another of the Kreis villages, sitting among the rural storekeepers, and the farmers who had come in from the land to hear the *Bürgermeister* and the *Landrat* speak. And when the *Bürgermeister* and the *Landrat* would have had their say, and the men and the few women present begun to leave the hall, Rod Murray would jump up and seek to make his protest heard, and not succeed, and climb up on a chair to say it, standing tall, and slouch-shouldered, and a little too heavy, in his gray tweed suit among them, knowing this was no part of the job for which his government paid him, but simply part of man's commitment to his fellow man.

"Say, this is an open forum!" he would call out loudly, and without fear, in his shameless rendering of their traditional tongue. "Now it's the time when questions are asked!" he would try to say, as he combed his fingers wildly through his dark, crisp, wavy hair. And the storekeepers, and the peasants, the women among them wearing their regional dress, would turn their heads to stare at him, not in censure, or in ridicule, but merely stare, their bland eyes vacant even of curiosity. And Rod Murray would jump down from the chair, and shoulder his way forward to where the *Bürgermeister* and the *Landrat* would be putting on their heavy coats. "This is the time for the people to ask you questions about the local administration!" he would cry out in his ringing voice. "This is the time for them to air their views and argue with you!" he would say. And the *Bürgermeister* and the *Landrat* would glance at the massively framed clock above the platform and one or the other of them, lowering his voice, might say that this was the way the meetings had always been held. What kind of questions had he had in mind, they might ask him in quiet, conciliatory voices, saying, as they buttoned their coats over, that once the official addresses had been delivered, it was customary for a town meeting to come to a close. And the young man who had been brought up among community

236

chests, and cooperatives in the Midwest, would stand there saying helplessly: "But this is a forum for the people! That's the idea of it," his dark, outraged eyes watching the people who had never asked questions of their administrators, and who could not learn to ask them now, turn quietly and go.

But once in the winter, when the snow was falling thick and fast, Rod Murray undertook with impatience an errand which had nothing to do with the mission on which he had come. It was dusk when he set out, for he had put this off until the final moment of the day, and he walked with his overcoat collar turned up, and the limp brim of his worn, felt hat pulled down, following a narrow, cobbled street which wound up through the archaic houses, begrudging every instant of the time that he must give. But he liked the taste of the winter evening on his lips, and the sight of the crowded, leaning dwelling places, so picturesque that it seemed to him he moved through that miniature scenery, and that facsimile of falling snow, which are contained within a paperweight glass ball. He climbed steadily, his eyes seeking the number of a house he did not know. It had been described in the telephone directory as the *Berufsschule für Bewegungs-Ausdruck-Kunst-Rhythmik und Gesellschaftstanz* but there was no sign to confirm this when he came to it, nor was there a bell to be found in the archway's moist, grooved stone. He lifted the knocker on the heavy oak panel of the door, and let it fall, and the ring of its iron sounded in the narrow, snow-hushed street. When the door had opened just wide enough to let him pass, Rod Murray stepped into the flagstoned corridor, and he waited a moment, wondering at the identifiable sense of stealth, the silence, which dwelt within the dancing school's interior. An oil lamp burned at the end of the long hall, and, to the left, a flight of dilapidated stairs leaned against the massive stones of the wall, its baroque banisters hanging, like a great, warped harp, no longer fit for music, forgotten there in the obscurity. And as the half dark cleared, he saw that a woman stood with her back against the door that she had closed behind him, and for an instant he felt the familiar stir of hope that, not Kant, or Fichte, or Hegel, but this unknown figure, this still unprobed segment of the national mind, the national experience, might yield some portion of the national mystery.

"I'm Mr. Murray, from Military Government," he said, speaking his imitation German to the faceless and nameless presence of the woman in the hall.

"I am the *Frau Direktor* of this poor little establishment," she said hoarsely and rapidly out of the shadows to him; and at the sound of her voice, defensive, cautious, low, he knew it would not be she who had cupped in her bare hands, and shielded through the years, the small, hot, eager flame of individual intent, keeping it clear of the collective blasphemy. "I used to have a big house in Hamburg, with three fine reception rooms, all good enough for royalty, and now it's come to this," she said, the whine resorted to at once, like an arm already slyly lifted in the darkness to ward off whatever threatened blow might fall. "I lost the house, and two concert grand pianos in the bombings. I used to have a fine selection of pupils, girls from decent families, but since the war ended, everything's changed. The quality's not the same," she said, and when she spoke again the voice was even warier. "Have you come privately, or is this an official visit you're making us?" she said.

"It's like this," said Rod Murray quickly, impatient with her voice, her words, her flesh. "One of our Military Govern-

238

ment officers is leaving, and we're giving him a party on Friday night, a sort of *Aufwiedersehen Abend*," he said, inventing the German phrase for it as he went along. "I've been asked to take care of the entertainment for the evening, and I was told you had dancers here, professional dancers—girls, of course. As a professional, you'll have to help me," he said, and he tried to see the hour marked on the watch strapped to his wrist. "This is the first time I've had to do anything in the line of entertainment," he said.

"Ah, girls," said the woman, and she seemed to speak in singular relief. "Sometimes the Army sends someone to investigate, so we have to ask. Will you come upstairs, Mr. Murray?" she said, and she moved out of the dark of the doorwell, saying: "Ah, girls. They're mostly *Flüchtlings* or D.P.s now. We haven't much else to offer," as she gathered up her hanging garments and moved swiftly past him to the stairs. He followed her up the trembling structure, having scarcely glimpsed her face yet, and, at the top, without warning, her profile was cast in outsized shadow on the wall. The features he saw were not those of a woman, but of a lean, lipless courtier from another century, an aging page boy, the scrawny hireling of knights in armor, with the hair cut like a casque to fit the bony head. The silhouetted nose was the beak of a bird of prey, and was perhaps even corneous in substance, Rod Murray thought in revulsion as the outlandish figure stooped, bowed and evil, to fit a key into the lock of the closed door. "There'll certainly be one or two to interest you," she said, and then she pushed the door open, and gestured with one horny wing for him to pass.

The big room they entered was as cold as a cave, and it was lit by four standing lamps which flanked both sides of an upright piano, with the coats of arms of the leading German cities embossed in color on their parchment shades. On the piano top stood a glass vase of crepe-paper roses, and when Rod Murray laid his hat down beside the vase, he saw that the rose petals, which had probably once been red, had faded to lavender beneath a film of dust and age.

"I know exactly what I want," he began to say briskly, while he sought to avoid the sight of the hostess reflected from every angle in the long, scarred mirrors which hung on two of the four moldy walls. "I thought of starting off with a Spanish or Hungarian dancer, if you had the right person and the correct music for it. Perhaps a fandango," he said, but wherever he looked for gaiety and beauty, there was the aged woman in her hanging, fanning clothes. Her brow was covered by a smooth, oiled, ebony bang which a green silk ribbon held in place, and from under this fringe, her black eyes watched him narrowly. Two spots of rouge, as dark as bruises, stood high upon her cheekbones, and within the shadow of the grotesquely hooked nose, the thin lips of a medieval lackey were painted mauve, and given a shape that was not theirs, so that they might seem athirst for sensuality. A green brocaded neckcloth kept the disaster of her throat from sight, but the fleshless cartilage of her ears was visible through the dyed black tassels of her hair. "Then perhaps follow this with a *romantisches* number, a *Herzen und Blumen* sort of thing," Rod Murray tried to go on with it as he strolled restlessly from lamp to piano, piano to mirror, mirror to lamp again, in this room which held itself in readiness for some function that he could not name. "You might have some acts to suggest, but I don't want to undertake too much. I'd like to know the price beforehand," he said, not knowing yet that this was the first sentence she had understood in its entirety, and understood by instinct only, with her eye turned canny as a hawk's eye under the oiled ebony fringe of hair.

"I'll get the girls down, and you can make your arrangements with them," she said. "But I get twenty per cent of every fee. That's customary in the establishment," she said, before she flapped from the room, and closed the door, and locked it from the landing. It was then, without any sense of shock or personal outrage, that he recognized the actual nature of the place, and he began to laugh. In his pocket were the two most recent letters from a college girl he knew at home, and he put his hand inside his overcoat and touched the folded thickness of them now.

While he waited, Rod Murray decided on the things that he was going to say. But he did not say any of them, for when the woman unlocked the door again, there were three girls with her, two of them blond, and the third one dark, and all of them identically dressed in flesh-colored bathing suits, with high-heeled, worn, black slippers on their naked feet. She herded them forward, these three white glutted geese, and, as they moved toward the piano, Rod Murray could see the goose-pimples the cold had raised on their plucked bare backs and on their heavy, undressed limbs. The two blond girls halted beside one of the standing lamps, and laid their arms around each other's waists, and faced Rod Murray, smiling, while the dark young woman sat down before the keyboard, flexed the muscles of her forearms, and began to play. As she played, the three of them chanted "Deep in the Heart of Texas" as casually as if the twang and the drawl, and the broken rhythm, were inherent in their birthright, and this accent from one state of America the flavor of their native speech. The hostess had taken a chair facing the piano, and, while the others sang to its accompaniment, she kept time by tapping her wooden leg, or her cloven hoof, or her broomstick, on the dusty boards.

"But this isn't the kind of thing I'm looking for!" Rod Murray cried out, and he retrieved his hat from the piano top, where it left a ring of melted snow. "I wanted dancers! I didn't come to waste my time with this! I wanted professional entertainers!" he said to them in his fury before he hastened toward the door. When he turned the key in the lock, and jerked the door open, the sound of the *Frau Direktor's* tapping, and the rippling of the music ceased, and the women were left there, motionless, speechless, hearing him shout: "Dancers! *Herr Gott*, can't you understand German?", before he jammed his hat on his head, and went running down the leaning stairs.

That was Thursday, and by Friday morning the snow was two feet deep in the streets of the town, and the gray tiled roofs of the *Schloss* and the university buildings, and the houses on the north side of the hill, were crested and fishboned with white. But although the sky was overcast, the snow had ceased to fall. Rod Murray gave no thought to the dancers as he walked through the snow to the *Rathaus*, where the trial of the former editor of the local newspaper was about to begin, for he had seen the articles the Nazi editor had written in the war years and these were in his mind as he pushed his way into the crowded courtroom, and shouldered his way forward, the only American who had taken the obligation as his own, and come. The defendant, sitting side by side with his lawyer, faced the German judge's raised seat, and the prosecutor strolled back and forth in the space left between the court stenographers and the defendant, rubbing his red-knuckled hands together, for he too had just come in from the streets of freshly fallen snow. The defendant was a lean, distinguished, white-haired gentleman, and at times he turned in his chair to smile discreetly, under his clipped moustaches, at his wife and his three daughters, clad in black, who sat behind him. Around these women, the defendant's friends formed a protective block, for the former editor was a celebrated and respected man.

"The defendant has stated, and maintains, that he was an anti-Nazi editor," were the words the prosecutor now addressed to the courtroom, and Rod Murray, wearing his overcoat still, usurped a place on the fringe of the elite, two rows behind the defendant's wife, and the chair cried out beneath his weight as he sat down. "As late as March, 1945, the defendant was still editing the newspaper in this town," the prosecutor said, and now a murmuring became audible, a whisper of protest which seemed to spread from seat to seat, stirring even from those who stood, packed close, in the back of the hall. "As a part of his defense, he has stated that his editorials were not political, but theological in nature," the prosecutor continued. "For an example, at Easter, 1945, the defendant wrote and published an editorial on the rising of the new Messiah from the grave." It was known that the prosecutor was not a native of the university town, that he was not a Hessian even, but that he was a *Flüchtlinge* from Rostock who had taken refuge here less than a year ago among them, and they did not like his alien accent, or the sharp, sad features of his face. "Now let us assume," the prosecutor said, giving half of all he had to say to the grave, young judge who looked down at them from his raised chair, and half to the peopled courtroom, "that there were certain unmistakable ways in which an anti-Nazi editor conducted himself so that he should be known for what he was." And now the prosecutor's dark glance rested upon the conservatively but expensively accoutred figure of the white-haired editor, and the spectators, too, turned toward him, some of them half rising from their seats the better to see this distinguished man whose printed words had for so long made plausible, and continued to make plausible even in defeat, the legend of their own ascendancy. Here he sat like a common man, and yet so manifestly the gentleman, despite the circumstances which had brought him here to be humbled in their eyes. But, although his two sons were prisoners of war in Russia still, as were the sons of many in the courtroom, and although his house, as was the case with so many of their houses, was still in the hands of the Americans, they knew that his very blood forbade that he become as common or as humble as they. "The question with which we are faced is whether the defendant, at any time, or by any voluntary act, gave evidence of being an anti-Nazi editor," the prosecutor was saying, and the murmuring now rose louder than before.

"Give us another prosecutor!" a voice called out, but scarcely a single voice, for it seemed to come from all four corners of the hall. "We don't need any *Flüchtlinge* here!" the multiple, disembodied voices called, and the young judge cleared his throat and asked for quiet, while the court guards moved through the assemblage. "We don't want anyone from the Eastern Zone to prosecute our townspeople!" the voices said. The judge had got to his feet, and he glanced uncertainly across the courtroom; but he, like the prosecutor, was a man without legal training, except that acquired in these Occupation-sanctioned courts, and it was little comfort to him now that he had been chosen for his political integrity. He stood up, shabby, provincial-looking, in his brown suit of ersatz, wartime wool, unfitted, to the eyes which had just turned from the defendant, for this or any other role which the Occupation might authorize him to play.

"There is in the courtroom now another newspaper editor!" the prosecutor's voice rang strongly out, and, at the sound of its authority, the uproar abruptly died. "I would like him to tell you his experiences. I am going to put him on the witness stand," he said. "I believe he will tell you that, in his opinion, it was not possible for a man to be both an anti-Nazi and a newspaper editor as late as 1945 in Germany."

The witness in question stood up at once in the front row of seats, a broad, short young man with thick-lensed glasses on his nose, wearing a suit that was too tight for him. And, as he picked his way nearsightedly across the intervening people, a titter of laughter ran through the courtroom, and the people did not draw their legs aside to let the witness pass. Once he had been sworn in by the court, he took his place before them in the isolated witness chair.

"I began publishing a political and literary weekly in Nuremberg in 1930. I was eighteen years old at the time," he began his testimony. He had clasped his childishly dimpled hands across the straining buttons of his vest, and a crescent of flesh, which lay pink and fresh beneath his chin, shrunk and expanded, deflated, inflated, as if made of rubber, while he spoke. "Until 1937, I experienced increasing trouble with the Reich authorities," he said, and his voice was pitched almost ludicrously high. "I had frequently refused to print the *Deutsches Nachrichten Büro* communiqués because of their distortion of the news. Early in 1937, I was informed through the *Gauleiter's* office that an impending paper shortage would necessitate the suspending of a large number of small newspapers, and that only those which served the interests of the nation, and the party, could count on sufficient newsprint to go on. In my editorials, I continued to criticize both the domestic and the foreign policy of the regime," he went on in his absurdly pitched voice, "so that it was only a matter of weeks before my offices were permanently closed. It seemed essential to me that all information concerning the restrictions on freedom of speech and action which were being imposed on the German people by the leaders of the Reich should be made known to the outside world, and I succeeded in passing weekly articles into Holland, and these were printed throughout the country, signed by my initials only," he said, and the rosy crescent which doubled his chin, deflated and then inflated, as he spoke. At this moment, as if roused suddenly to interest, the defendant stirred in his chair, and his flat, naked lips stiffened in a half smile of forbearance beneath his white moustache. Then he leaned a little closer to his lawyer, and dropped his lean, gentlemanly hand upon the other's sleeve. The lawyer listened to the communication that was whispered to him, nodding his round head slowly in agreement, his prominent, blue eyes fixed without expression on the ludicrous figure seated in the witness chair. "In the spring of 1940, when the Wehrmacht overran Holland," the witness continued, "my identity as the author of these articles was revealed in the files of an Amsterdam newspaper, and I was arrested in Nuremberg shortly after that. I was tried, and sentenced to fifteen years at hard labor," he said, and then he ceased to speak.

"Will you give the court some of the details concerning your internment?" the prosecutor said.

"I was interned in Dachau. My windpipe was broken during the beatings I received there," he said, his eyes myopic, undecipherable, behind the thick lenses of his spectacles, and no emotion altered his smooth, fat, fair-skinned face. "I had served nearly a third of my sentence when I was liberated by the Americans," he said, making the statement without drama, but, once it was made, the defense lawyer arose.

"If Your Honor permits," he said, the title given in derision to the judge who wore no judicial robes, "I would like to suggest that we who are gathered here today bow our heads before the witness's martyrdom. It is evident to everyone of us that this young man must have suffered the greatest privations during his confinement as a traitor to his country. Perhaps it would be in order to take up a collection for him in the courtroom today. My client has expressed himself as willing to start off such a subscription with a donation of two Deutschmarks and fifty pfennigs to enable this needy man to buy himself a hearty meal."

The laughter appeared to begin just behind the defendant's chair, and it was echoed here and there throughout the courtroom, until, gaining momentum, it seemed to rise from the throat of every man and woman in the ancient hall. The young judge again called out for quiet, but now that the witness had got to his feet, the spectators only laughed the louder, as if, standing there erect, with his short arms straining in the sleeves of his jacket, he was an even more humorous figure than they had recalled.

"Quiet!" the judge admonished them, but the tumult and

247

the laughter rose, and there was no sign or semblance of quiet. Instead, the multiple voice which had spoken out before now gathered power and articulation, and it cried "Heil Hitler!", and the judge leapt up, his young hands trembling, and ordered that the court be cleared.

It was only Rod Murray who moved against the refluent tide, making his way steadily back through the loquacious groups as they drifted toward the exits, past the defendant's wife, the defendant's daughters, the defendant himself, who stood chatting amiably with the local dentist and the owner of the requisitioned hotel. He shouldered his way, in an overcoat bought four years ago in Chicago, back toward the tables where the court stenographers gathered their papers up, and past them to the judge, and the witness, and the prosecutor, knowing that in making his way to them, he approached the flesh and the blood of men who spoke his tongue. And yet there was nothing he could find to say in shame or in anger or in any language to them, but, until the courtroom cleared, he stood there, taking his place beside them, and then they walked out into the sunless day together. On the steps of the *Rathaus* he turned to them, as if to brothers, and he shook the judge's, and the witness's, and the prosecutor's hands.

He ate lunch alone at the Special Services Club, and, with the taste of coffee in comfort on his tongue still, he came out onto the high, bleak terrace of the club. The terra-cotta flower-boxes stood empty on the balustrades, and across the valley of this foreign land of Hesse, the *Schloss* stood strong as a fortress on its hill. It might have been a picture that Breughel had painted, all this which lay before him, the slate-blue houses of the town descending, roof by snow-traced roof, to the barren trees which bordered the dark waters of the

river, with even the single crow set as trademark and signature in the leafless branches, except that the bright, myriad,
scattered presence of the living, which was the speech of
Breughel's heart, had been deleted from the scene. And in a
month like this one, Rod Murray thought as he leaned on the
balustrade in the chill, gray light of afternoon, he had flown
with the others before dawn up this valley, by-passing the
university town, and the others before it, the steel hearts of the
engines throbbing northward as they crossed these hills toward Kassel, moving in formation toward what they had come
out to do. It was no more than one name recalled out of many
destinations, remembered now because of the look of the sky
and the river, and because he knew that below, at the bridge
which spanned the water, a sign stated that Kassel lay no
more than a hundred kilometres ahead. Kassel, he thought,
hearing again the pulse of the bombers as they bore such
annihilation to that one town that the dust and the débris, and
the broken galleries and pilasters of where it once had stood,
had no more relation to the present than the hushed, volcanic
twilight of Pompeii. And then, without warning, he remembered the dancers, and remembered the farewell party would
take place that evening, and he fled quickly down the red
sandstone steps of the club terrace to hail the Army bus which
passed below.

In his office in the Military Government building, his German secretary was putting fresh varnish on her nails, so she
could not look up at once when he came in. But she said that
the *Herr Direktor* of the local theatre company was putting
on a Zuckmayer play which called for a Luger automatic to
be fired on the stage. As long as Germans could not be in
possession of firearms, she went on saying as she painted the

nail varnish carefully on, the *Herr Direktor* had been trying all morning to get in touch with him to find out what he should do.

"That's something for the Provost Marshal's office," Rod Murray said, dismissing it.

"Oke-doke, but it seems it comes under Art Information," said the secretary, surveying her nails. "The Provost Marshal's office sent him down to us."

There was this to be settled, and it took four telephone calls, and an hour and a half of time, and there followed a conference with the *Führer* of "The Nature Lovers" as to which numbers of their repertoire of marching songs would be authorized, under the relaxing of controls, to be sung at future meetings in the springtime hills. It was five o'clock, it was the end of the day, when the young *Führer* left Rod Murray's office, and there had been no time to think of the entertainment for the evening that lay ahead. And then Rod Murray's secretary came in to comb out her long hair at the mirror before going home, and she said that someone from the *Berufsschule für Bewegungs-Ausdruck-Kunst-Rhythmik und Gesellschaftstanz* had telephoned.

"My God, the dancers! The entertainers for the party to-night!" Rod Murray cried, and he jumped up behind his desk.

"Would you like me to take care of it for you?" said his secretary, and she looked at her own face in the mirror as she combed back her hair.

"I wanted Hungarian, Spanish, dancers—in costume, of course!" Rod Murray cried out. "And musicians with their music! I wanted to make it something good—"

"I can make it good," said his secretary. She had turned

away from the glass on the wall, and he saw her hair, as he had seen it countless times before, combed dark and soft to her shoulders, and the lipstick laid smoothly on her mouth. "I've been working six months for you, and you still don't seem to understand me," she said, her eyes on him in stubborn, cold rebuke. "The other officers I worked for here before were different. They all seemed to understand me," she said, and she came across the room toward his desk, American nylons pulled tight and sheer upon her well-shaped legs. Then she picked up the short black arm of mouthpiece and receiver from the telephone, and she dialled the numbers with a forefinger on which the nail was varnished as bright as blood. The conversation took a quarter of an hour, and while she asked the questions, and gave the answers, her dark, slow glance moved, without expression, upon the features of his face. And when it was done, she sat, in the green plaid skirt that must have been ordered from a Sears, Roebuck catalogue page by whom, or at what interval in the history of Military Government, or for what compensation, he did not know, and she told him what the *Frau Direktor* of the *Berufsschule* had said. She said it was only after he had gone down the stairs the night before that the *Frau Direktor* had understood he had come there for dancers, professional dancers. "You need someone to take care of you over here. You have too much faith in people. I saw that right away, the minute I started working for you," his secretary said, and she threw her head back, and shook out her long soft hair.

"All right," said Rod Murray in impatience. "What else did the *Frau Direktor* say?"

"She said that some stars of a well-known troupe of dancers had arrived from Berlin this afternoon, and she could send you some very cosmopolitan performers, if you wanted them still," she said. She had slipped off the corner of the desk now, and she looked at him with suddenly baleful eyes. "I told her to send them to Military Government billets at eight o'clock tonight, with costumes and musicians."

"How much did you settle for?" Rod Murray said, as he watched her going, as if in pique, to the door.

"Fifty Deutschmarks, including the music," his secretary said, "and the money to be paid directly to her. She's afraid they might hold out on her percentage," and then her voice stretched lazily into irony. "You should call on me more often. I'm pretty good at making bargains," she said.

It was after eight by the time Rod Murray had eaten, and bathed, and dressed, and he was eager for a sight of the entertainers as he came down the stairs. This requisitioned house in which he and the others were billeted was one of the finest houses in town, richly furnished, and handsomely wainscoted and beamed, without a mark of wartime damage on it. And now the lower floor of it was decked out for the farewell party with paper vines of mauve wisteria, and hanging, cardboard stars. A distant banquet table, framed by the dark wood of the wide arched doorways which opened from room to room, could be seen, laid with white linen, in the farthest chamber which once had been the Nazi owner's library. From the stairs, Rod Murray saw the shining glass goblets placed there in preparation, and the punch bowl, still empty, and the Meissner porcelain waiting, the monogrammed silver laid spoon within gleaming spoon, fork curved to fork, beneath the oscillating shadows of the hanging stars. From the kitchen alone, where the servants prepared the buffet supper, came the sound of the living; for the Senior Military Government Officer, and the

Criminal Investigation Agent, and the Legal and University Officers, were dressing in their bedrooms still, and the guests had not yet arrived.

Only when he had reached the last step of the stairs did Rod Murray see there were two people sitting side by side on the carved bench in the entrance hall. He took them at first for children, so slight, so submissive, they seemed as they sat there under the massive, mounted stag heads: a pale-haired boy in an opera cloak, with the velvet collar fastened beneath his pointed chin, and a girl in a long, dark shabby coat, drawn close beside him, her body curved as if in weariness, and a muff of black and white rabbit fur upon her knees. The muff was large enough for a deep-breasted *diva* to have carried in triumph, and the girl kept her hands within it, and a bunch of shrivelled, faded violets, made of cloth, was pinned to its molting hide. They were abandoned children, Rod Murray thought, who had put on these adult clothes to give themselves stature and authority for one evening, but not in any spirit of carnival, for their faces, which were turned toward him, were strangely austere. But once they had got to their feet, and stood before him on the delicately tinted Persian rug, he saw they were doubtless his own age, perhaps in their middle twenties, but so frail that he believed he could have lifted them, one in each arm, with ease, and carried them across the hall like dolls.

"The *Frau Direktor* of the *Berufsschule*," the young man began saying in German in a low voice to Rod Murray.

"Yes, yes," Rod Murray said quickly. He took his cigarettes out, and he passed them first to the girl, the stirring of hope quickening in him again, believing it might be from their mouths that he would learn how it had taken place, and how it had seemed to them when they were children, and how much had been explained away so that the human ear could bear to hear the rest. He stood close to the girl now, and her head reached barely to his shoulder, and her hair was wrenched up from her small, swollen brow, and combed into a pompadour, and the long, faded, golden ends of it pinned high upon her skull. Her fingers came, as sharp as a bird's claws, from the rabbit muff, and she did not speak, she did not smile, but her hand, with the cigarette in the fingers of it, withdrew inside the muff again. Her narrow lips were not so much as touched with red, but her dark eyes were outlined and lashed so lavishly and carelessly with mascara in her white, pointed face, that Rod Murray had the illusion that he viewed them through a magnifying glass. "Yes, of course, I was expecting you," he said, and he passed the cigarettes to the young man, whose bony hand tossed one wing of the opera cloak aside and sought to unhook the worn, velvet collar at his throat, as an actor, beginning his big scene and finding stage fright parching his tongue might fumble desperately for breath.

"Perhaps the *Frau Direktor* told you that my wife and I come from the eastern sector of Berlin?" he said, and he bowed his head to light his cigarette from the lighter Rod Murray held.

"The food situation is pretty grim there, isn't it?" said Rod Murray, but the young man did not answer, for it was not the role of *Flüchtlinge* which they were here to play.

"We've just had a most successful night-club season there," he said, and now, with a cigarette between his fingers, his tongue seemed eased, and he drew the good, sustaining draughts of the tobacco in.

"We have our costumes with us," the girl said, speaking scarcely aloud, and, with her hand inside the molting muff still, she gestured behind them toward the bench. And there, in the shadows against the panelled wall, Rod Murray saw the trademark of those who wander the autobahns in flight, or who sit beneath the bridges, waiting for nothing but a destination—the split, bulging shape of a suitcase, its material varnished to simulate leather, its bulk supported by various lengths and weights of string. "We like to travel," the girl said, with these words refusing their part in that dogged exodus of women and men who crossed illicitly from one zone to the other for the sake of food, or for the opulent look of counters and store windows, or else for the indescribable quality of freedom, either breathed or spoken, the stragglers coming at the rate of a thousand a month, some said, and others put it at closer to a hundred a day.

"The *Frau Direktor* of the *Berufsschule* is my wife's aunt. That's how we happened to stop off in Hesse," the young man said, and, as he smoked the cigarette, he smiled at the thought of this part of the country's rural ignorance, its archaic monuments, its bigotry. "We'll probably stay a little while with her, although there's not much of interest for us here," he said, and he added: "My wife's aunt is Jewish. My wife and I are neither Jews nor refugees."

"We're planning a foreign tour—France, England, and then America," the girl said.

"Look," said Rod Murray, speaking quickly as he glanced at the time upon his wrist; "before you people begin dancing, maybe you'd like something to eat—some sandwiches and coffee? If you wouldn't mind coming into the kitchen," he began, but they must have sensed the weakness, the perturbation in him, for their eyes were on him in slow, cold calculation, examining this which he had just proposed.

"So you're going to pay us in food and cigarettes, then?" the young man said. The three of them stood motionless in the hallway, as hushed as if in the deep heart of a forest, waiting beneath the dead stags' lifted, antlered heads.

"That wasn't the arrangement," the girl said, her thin lips scarcely seeming to move.

"But, of course not. Of course, you'll get paid the Deutschmarks too," Rod Murray said, and he turned to lead them toward the kitchen.

"And you'll pay it to us?" the young man said, not moving. "You won't pay it to the *Frau Direktor?*" he said.

They were almost at the threshold of the kitchen, with the fragrance of fresh coffee coming richly on the air, when the young man remembered the cardboard suitcase, and he walked swiftly back in his cracked patent-leather dancing pumps to pick it up and bear it with him before anyone should carry it away.

The next to come were the musicians. There were three of them—one with a shining bald pate, and a leather music portfolio in his hand, and two studious-looking young men, one carrying a violin in its case, and the other an accordion. They were all three members of the local symphony orchestra, the violinist told Rod Murray, giving his classical right profile to the conversation, with his eyes fixed straight ahead, like the set gaze of the blind. But he was not blind, for he laid his violin case down on the bench, and he took off his overcoat, as the others did, and then the three of them strung their identical white silk scarves through the sleeves of their overcoats, and they hung them in the cloakroom, and then they raised their open palms, and even the bald-pated musician made the gesture of smoothing back his hair. When this was

256

done, they followed Rod Murray across the polished bare floor of the first reception room, where the grand piano stood, the violinist carrying his violin in its case, and the accordionist his accordion on its plaited leather strap, and the pianist the music portfolio. But it was only the violinist, keeping one half of his face averted still, who looked up and smiled at the sight of the wisteria, and the hanging silver cardboard stars.

"It will be spring soon," the violinist said, speaking his carefully enunciated English to Rod Murray, and there was a sound of happiness in his voice, as if he had recognized in these tokens that a long, cold season was about to change. He and the accordionist were students at the university, he said; they were medical students, and he still turned his head from Rod Murray as he lifted his instrument from its case. It would begin to be more pleasant now, walking up the paths to the lecture halls, he went on saying, and he asked Rod Murray how well he knew the town, and the *Schloss*, and the short cuts leading through the trees. "There is a quite lonely statue of Schiller. It stands among the lilacs halfway up," he said, and he dropped his head, in seeming solicitude, upon the violin's vibrant wood.

The bald-pated man had sat down in his ancient dinner suit on the concave seat of the piano stool, and now he jumped up, and spun the seat on its swivel, and seated himself again, his short legs reaching for the pedals, his blunt fingers stroking the keys. The accordionist lifted his accordion, ornate in ivory and gold, and cradled it in love in his arms for a moment while he peered across the pianist's shoulder at the open score.

"The dancers are changing into their costumes," Rod Murray said, and now, as the violinist tuned his strings, he saw for the first time, and with an almost convulsive sense of shock, the left side of the violinist's face. The head was a classical, rather noble head, constructed of long, solid bones, and crowned with a mane of lightish, lively hair. But the face he saw now was the face of a broken statue, for a scar ran hideously from the lobe of the left ear, slashed into the shattered temple, and crossed the forehead, a welt that served to seam the cavity where the hinge of jaw and cheekbone had functioned once, but where hinge and cheekbone were no longer, and mounted to stitch the empty temple closed. "They're going to do a tango, a rhumba, and a Viennese waltz," Rod Murray said, with his heart gone sick within him. "Let's go out and have a drink before they start," he said. And so it became the violinist's turn to follow, as had the dancers before him, into the kitchen, and there, in his abomination of this face, Rod Murray filled the two tall glasses with Rhine wine. "So you're medical students?" Rod Murray said, keeping his eyes away.

"*Prosit*," the violinist said before he drank, and he went on saying: "We will be doctors. We will cure humanity," saying it partly in humor to the American. "I know a strange story about doctors, about surgeons," he said, speaking a little shyly of this thing he knew. "In the war, you know, the doctors, the surgeons, did great things with plastic surgery. They could make a man's face new again. They could make it look like something it had not been before. My father was a surgeon, an Army surgeon, and he did this," the violinist said, and Rod Murray stood listening to what he said, his eyes fixed on the label on the slender bottle. "But after a time, he found out that a man's face does not stay the way that surgery makes it. After six months, eight months, a man's face will change back again to what he is like himself, inside. If you are a poet,"

258

said the violinist as he lifted his glass of wine and drank, "then an Army surgeon, a good Army surgeon, has his duty to perform, and when he operates he must give you a warrior's face. My father did this. But in six months, eight months, the face he has made becomes a poet's face again."

"That is fantasy," Rod Murray said, but he felt this knowledge chilling his blood.

"No, it is the truth," said the violinist, and he put down his glass so that Rod Murray could fill it with white wine again. "If you do not believe this is true, then there is nothing left to believe," he said. "My face," he said abruptly. "They left it the way it is because by that time they had learned. They knew they could make it look the way they wanted, and then in six months, eight months, it would betray them again. It would look like a musician's face, or a poet's face. It would have the old mark of loneliness on it, and this they could not have."

Their glasses stood empty on the kitchen table when they walked back into the reception room together, and the violinist smiled, as if at some secret which he alone possessed, as he moved the floor lamp a little closer to the piano, and adjusted the shade of it so that the light fell on the tilted rack where the open book of music stood. Above them could be heard the slamming of bedroom doors on the upper floors, and then the goodnatured chaffing of the other Military Government officers as they came down the wainscoted stairs. And then the bell at the entrance door rang loudly, and the first guests were ushered into the hallway, the American women in long, half-formal gowns, and the men, in Army uniform or in fancy jackets from the Clothing Store, coming in with a clamor of greeting from the wintry night. Once their wraps had been laid aside, the guests moved on, escorted by the Public Safety Officer, or the Criminal Investigation Agent, or the Legal or University Officers, to the farthest room where the platters were laid with heart-shaped sandwiches, and the punch bowl stood filled now to the brim.

The musicians had begun playing "Don Giovanni," to set the romantic tempo of the evening, but once the dancers appeared dramatically in Spanish costume in the doorway, the piano, the accordion, and the violin, took their cue, and they broke into the triumphant bars of "Toreador." And now that the dancers danced, Rod Murray could scarcely bring himself to look in their direction, for they were far too thin to be making this spectacle of themselves in any public place. It seemed to him that the threads of their necks must snap in two, unable to bear the weight of the fleshless skulls they carried, and that their bones would pierce the carnival lace and tinsel of their disguise, and expose them for the skeletons they were. He could hear the girl's hand striking the tambourine with which she danced, and he could not bring himself to turn his head and see again the bony stalks of her white arms lifted, like the arms of those who have already perished reaching from the grave. And the young man, in his matador's suit and his cracked, black, patent-leather pumps, danced his desperate, intricate steps before her, his legs as brittle and thin as sticks of kindling in his cotton stockings, the brass coins jingling with avarice on his tricorne hat. And no one else looked at them, it seemed to Rod Murray; no one else dared watch them as they danced away across the parquet floor. In the farthest room, the Senior Military Government Officer was urging the guests to drink, and the waiters passed with trays among them, and the men's and women's talk and laughter sounded far, anonymous, without human meaning, under the festoons of Japanese wisteria, and the trembling pasteboard stars.

Then the Spanish number was done, and the dancers were gone, and the faint clapping of hands expired through the rooms, and Rod Murray asked that drinks be brought for the musicians, and he himself drank a goblet of punch quickly down.

"Let's give them a dance number now, so the guests can dance while the entertainers change," Rod Murray said, and he stayed near to the musicians, not wanting to meet the Senior Military Government Officer's offended eyes. "What front were you on when it happened?" he suddenly said, and he stood looking boldly at the violinist's face.

"Oh, that! I wasn't on any front," the violinst said, and he dropped his head, as if in apology, upon the violin's wood. "I lived in a town further up toward the north, a place called Kassel. I didn't have time to get to an air-raid shelter. I hadn't been in the Army long, and I hadn't seen any action yet. That's all there is to it," he said.

"Kassel," Rod Murray repeated. He set the cut-glass goblet down on the top of the grand piano, and he stood there, stunned for a moment, at the sound of the town's name. "Kassel. My God," he said. "You were in Kassel."

Before the musicians began to play, Rod Murray picked up the goblet again, and he finished the punch that was in it. And it seemed to him then that if the others, the Germans and the Americans alike, were to go away and leave them together for a little while, it was possible that something quite simple and comprehensible might still be said.

A Note on the Type

THE TEXT of this book was set on the Linotype in
JANSON, a recutting made direct from type cast
from matrices long thought to have been made by
the Dutchman Anton Janson, who was a practicing
type founder in Leipzig during the years 1668–87.
However, it has been conclusively demonstrated
that these types are actually the work of Nicholas
Kis (1650–1702), a Hungarian, who most probably
learned his trade from the master Dutch type
founder Dirk Voskens. The type is an excellent
example of the influential and sturdy Dutch types
that prevailed in England up to the time William
Caslon developed his own incomparable designs
from these Dutch faces.

Typography by
VINCENT TORRE

A Note about the Author

SINCE her birth in St. Paul, Minnesota, Kay
Boyle has done work in almost every field of
writing—fiction, poetry, fashion, translating,
reviewing, and writing for young people. She
won a Guggenheim Fellowship in 1934 and
again in 1961, and the O. Henry Memorial
Prize for the Best Short Story of the Year in
both 1934 and 1941. Among her more than
twenty-five published volumes are: *The White
Horses of Vienna; Gentlemen, I Address You
Privately; Three Short Novels; The Seagull on
the Step; Generation Without Farewell;* and
her revision of Robert McAlmon's autobiogra-
phy, *Being Geniuses Together, 1920–1930.* Since
1923 Kay Boyle has lived largely in France,
Austria, England, and Germany, and now
makes her home in San Francisco.